The Mathesis Series
Kenneth O. May, Editor

Ways of thought of great mathematicians
Herbert Meschkowski

Counterexamples in analysis
Bernard R. Gelbaum and John M. H. Olmsted

Ways of thought
of great mathematicians

An approach to the history of mathematics

by Herbert Meschkowski, Pädagogische Hochschule
and Free University, Berlin.
translated by John Dyer-Bennet,
Carleton College.

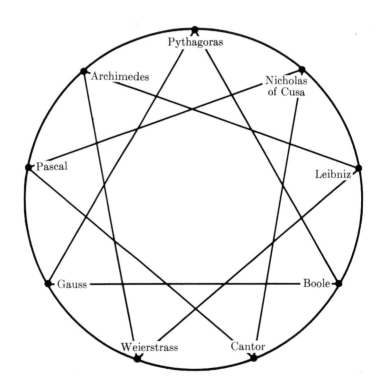

Holden-Day, Inc.: *San Francisco, London, Amsterdam*

1964

PICTURE CREDITS

The Bettman Archive: pages 1, 13, 33, 47, 61; Dover Publications:
page 91; Fratelli Alinari: page 25; Frederic Lewis: pages 71, 85.

Preface

To understand the fundamental problems of modern mathematics, one must first study the history of mathematics. The meaning of modern formalism is made clear by the difficulties which arose from the classical view of the nature of mathematics in the nineteenth century.

However, it is not easy for a modern mathematician to approach the history of his discipline. Most of the books on the subject try to give a comprehensive picture, omitting nothing of any importance. Thus in the thin volumes, catalogues of names and dates take up a large part of the space. Even in the longer books, the achievements of individual investigators can only be summarized.

For this reason it seems worthwhile to try to complement the invaluable comprehensive works (on one period or one person) with an approach to the history of mathematics of quite a different sort. I make no attempt at completeness. Instead I try, through fairly detailed discussions of a few examples, to bring to life the ways of thought of mathematicians of earlier centuries.

The choice of men is, of course, somewhat arbitrary. I might, for instance, have omitted Nicholas of Cusa and George Boole and taken up instead Newton and Euler. Nevertheless, I am quite willing to admit there is a principle in my selections. It is sometimes said that the modern mathematician lives in a sort of ghetto, in voluntary isolation, out of reach of problems which cannot be attacked by mathematical methods. In earlier times this was not true, and some of my examples were chosen to show this.

This does not mean that today we make mathematics the handmaiden of a metaphysics which purports to be scientific, as Georg Cantor once did, or that we should use it as a collection of examples for philosophical or theological deductions, in the fashion of Cusanus. That has hardly been possible since the crisis in the foundations of mathematics around the turn of the century. Today the contribution of mathematics to philosophy is of a different sort. It lies, as I see it*, in the area rather of epistemology than of metaphysics. A glance at the history of our subject is just the thing to make this shift plain.

Often, especially in the later chapters, I let the investigators speak for themselves. Three of the letters thus quoted are published here for the first time:

> The letter from H. A. Schwarz to Georg Cantor (Chap. VIII) and that from Georg Cantor to Father Esser (Chap. IX) were kindly put at my disposal by private individuals.

---

* See [A 12] (bibliography), Chap. XIII.

Preface

The letter from Georg Cantor to F. Goldscheider (Chap. IX) is in the State and University Library of Lower Saxony, in Göttingen.

It is hoped that the bibliography at the end of the book (reference numbers in square brackets) will stimulate the reader to further study.

Herbert Meschkowski
Berlin, June 1961

Table of contents

The Pythagoreans

The order   *2*
The Pythagorean numbers   *3*
The discovery of the Golden Section   *6*

Archimedes

The uses of mathematics   *14*
The surface of a sphere   *16*
A heuristic argument   *20*

Nicholas of Cusa

On informed ignorance   *26*
Squaring the circle   *28*

Blaise Pascal

The course of a prodigy   *34*
The principle of mathematical induction   *36*
On geometric proof   *43*

Gottfried Wilhelm Leibniz

The polyhistor   *48*
The "harmonic triangle"   *50*
Leibniz's series   *54*
The "infinitely small"   *57*

Carl Friedrich Gauss

"Prince of mathematicians"   *62*
An analytic proof of the Fundamental Theorem of Algebra   *64*

George Boole

The self-taught man   *72*
A new algebra   *74*
Application to probability   *79*
Boolean algebra today   *81*

Table of contents

Weierstrass and his school √
The arithmetization of analysis   *86*
A letter from H. A. Schwarz to Georg Cantor   *87*

Georg Cantor √
A disputed "paradise"   *92*
A letter from Georg Cantor to F. Goldscheider   *95*
Example of an uncountable set   *103*

Bibliography

Index of names

Ways of thought
of great mathematicians

The Pythagoreans

In fact, everything that can be known has number.
For it is not possible to conceive of or to
know anything that has not.

Philolaus of Croton ([I8], p. 77)

Pythagoras

The Pythagoreans

The order

The origins of mathematics lie in the mists of antiquity. The historian who wants to study the mathematics of ancient Egypt must gain his insights from the study of only three major documents and some fragments ([I 6], p. 15). These papyri were instructions for practical reckoning: they were to show officials how to compute interest, or the amount of grain needed to make a given quantity of bread.

Nevertheless, though its purpose is very practical, the Rhind papyrus begins with bold promises. It announces "proper entrance into the knowledge of all existing things and all obscure secrets." As a matter of fact, it contains only the "secrets" of how to multiply and divide. Behind this pretentious claim lies the belief, common in ancient cultures, that the laws of numbers have not only a practical meaning but also a mystical or religious one. We will find that belief again later, among the Pythagoreans.

It was the Greeks who, out of mystical numerology and the practical arts of measuring and reckoning, first developed the discipline based on axioms and proceeding by means of rigorous proofs, which today we call mathematics. Thus the age of the Pythagoreans is of particular importance for the historian of mathematics who is interested in the relations between cultures. Here are to be found primitive claims, alongside number-theoretic and geometric theorems which satisfy the demands of a modern mathematician.

Today we think of Pythagoras[1] as a mathematician. Most of his contemporaries thought otherwise. Herodotus considered him an "important sophist." Others knew him as the founder of a religious order about which many wonderful tales were told. Finally, the comedians presented the followers of Pythagoras as poor and dirty vegetarians, and said nothing about their mathematical accomplishments.

Little is known of the life of Pythagoras. It is probably true that in his youth he travelled as a student to Egypt. Perhaps he also spent some time in Babylon — the relation between Pythagorean and Babylonian arithmetic makes the conjecture plausible. About 530 B.C. he fled from the dictator Polycrates to Croton in northern Italy. There he is said to have gathered about him a circle of enthusiastic disciples. He preached to them the immortality of the soul, demanded a life of abstinence and moderation, and taught astronomy, mathematics, music and philosophy.

---

[1] ca. 580-500 B.C.

2

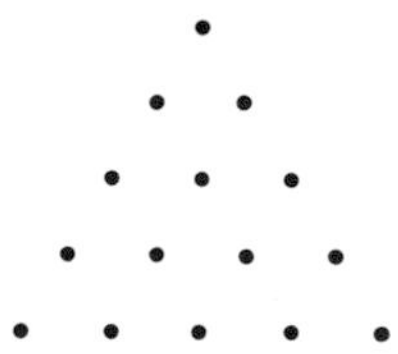

Fig. 1

To many of us today the close connection between religious or moral principles and mathematical propositions found in the Pythagorean order seems strange. For the Pythagoreans this unity was the foundation of their world view. According to their teachings God is one, and the multiplicity of the world can be understood by means of the laws of numbers. That was the great discovery of the Pythagoreans. Not only the paths of the stars but also the laws of musical harmony and architectural beauty are determined by simple ratios of whole numbers[2]: "The whole world is harmony and number."

We shall not go any further into the philosophical theories of the Pythagoreans, but shall concern ourselves with their mathematical accomplishments. For the modern historian of mathematics it is admittedly not easy to say anything with confidence about the origins of specific mathematical theorems or methods from that period. Of Pythagoras' own writings not a line has come down to us. Hence one cannot determine with any certainty which discoveries were made by the Master himself and which by his students. Because of the great admiration for the "miracle worker" Pythagoras, it is quite likely that later generations ascribed to him results actually obtained by his students or contemporaries. We shall confine ourselves to discussing, in some detail, two discoveries of the Pythagoreans.

The Pythagorean numbers

In his introduction to the lore of numbers, Nichomachus of Gerasa collected what the Pythagoreans knew of the laws of whole numbers. It is to be assumed that this work, written about 100 A.D., contains those results which are actually due to Pythagoras and his circle.

The Pythagoreans pictured the integers as groups of points like constellations. From such configurations one can read some remarkable number-theoretic laws. For example, Figure 1 shows the Triangular Numbers. The rows of the triangle contain 1, 2, 3, 4, . . . points, and the number of points in an n-rowed triangle is the sum of the first n positive integers. For example, $1 + 2 = 3, 1 + 2 + 3 = 6, 1 + 2 + 3 + 4 = 10$, etc. In this way the Pythagoreans obtained the well-known sequence of Triangular Numbers: 1, 3, 6, 10, 15, 21, 28, . . . Even more remarkable are the laws which can be read off from a square array (Figure 2). Clearly to a square array with n^2 points one must

---

[2] Note that the irrational numbers were unknown in Greek mathematics. "Ratios of numbers" are always ratios of whole numbers.

The Pythagoreans

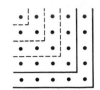

Fig. 2

add $n + 1 + n = 2n + 1$ points to get a square with $(n + 1)^2$ points. Thus

(1) $$n^2 + (2n + 1) = (n + 1)^2 .$$

From (1) we see that the differences between successive squares give the sequence of odd numbers. With the help of (1) we can also find sets of numbers a, b and c which satisfy the Pythagorean equation.

(2) $$a^2 + b^2 = c^2 .$$

To do this we need only make $2n + 1$ in (1) a square. If we let $2n + 1 = m^2$, then[3]

(3) $$n = \frac{m^2 - 1}{2}, \qquad n + 1 = \frac{m^2 + 1}{2} .$$

Substituting (3) in (1) we get

(4) $$m^2 + \left(\frac{m^2 - 1}{2}\right)^2 = \left(\frac{m^2 + 1}{2}\right)^2 .$$

For $m = 3, 5, 7, 9, \ldots$ equation (4) gives Pythagorean numbers a, b and c, that is, integers which satisfy equation (2):

m	a	b	c
3	3	4	5
5	5	12	13
7	7	24	25
9	9	40	41

Probably the Pythagoreans were led to discover the celebrated Pythagorean theorem[4] by such number-theoretic arguments rather than by comparison of areas.

Adding the successive positive integers leads, as we have seen, to the Triangular Numbers, while adding the successive odd numbers (see Figure 2) leads to the squares:

$$1 + 3 + 5 + \cdots + (2n - 1) = n^2 .$$

What sort of sequence do we get if we add the successive even numbers?

---

[3] Note that m^2 is odd, so the fractions in (3) are integers.
[4] This theorem on right triangles was known to the Indians. However, they probably had no proof of it.

Fig. 3

$$2 + 4 + 6 + 8 + \cdots + 2n = 2\,(1 + 2 + 3 + 4 + \cdots + n) = n(n + 1),$$
as can be seen by considering a rectangular configuration of $n(n + 1)$ numbers. Figure 3 shows the first four rectangular numbers in such an array. Adding odd numbers leads to a square schema, while adding even ones leads to a rectangle in which the ratio $(n + 1)/n$ of the sides depends on n.

Thus the odd numbers generate a limited number of forms (the square above), while the even ones generate a multiplicity of rectangles which are not similar. From this the Pythagoreans deduced the following correspondence:

$$\text{odd} \longleftrightarrow \text{limited}$$
$$\text{even} \longleftrightarrow \text{unlimited}$$

Of course, we would today no longer follow the Pythagoreans in drawing such conclusions. Nevertheless, one should respect the ways in which the modes of thought of past centuries differ from our own. It does not seem to us appropriate to speak here of "idle speculation" and "nonsense" ([A 6], p. 114). The Pythagoreans had a fault still common today: they made unsupported generalizations. This was true not only of the correspondences odd : limited and even : unlimited but also of their fundamental thesis "Everything is number."

A fine characteristic of mathematics is that it does not allow wild speculation to go unpunished. Sooner or later valid counterexamples make it plain that the investigator who generalized too boldly has erred. In the humanities, on the other hand, unsupported speculations sometimes have quite a long life; they cannot be so clearly refuted.

The discovery of incommensurable segments is perhaps the first example of how mathematics can veto too general a claim[5]. Soon after the Master's death the Pythagoreans discovered that in certain figures there were incommensurable segments, that is, segments the ratio of whose lengths could not be expressed in integers. The simplest example of such a pair of incommensurable segments is that of a side a and a diagonal d of a square. If there were integers p and q such that $d{:}a = p{:}q$, then since $d^2 = 2a^2$, 2 would have a rational square root : $\sqrt{2} = p/q$. It can easily be proved that this is not true[6].

---

[5] For further instances see, for example, [A 12].

[6] A proof can be found in [A 12], p. 10 ff. These counterexamples for the Pythagorean thesis came from the field of abstract mathematics. It must be admitted, however, that in atomic research modern physics continually encounters laws expressible in whole numbers. This supplies a sort of justification for the reasoning of the Pythagoreans.

The Pythagoreans

In scientific discoveries it is often not the first approach to new fields of investigation that proves the simplest. Thus the Pythagoreans first discovered incommensurable segments by studying the regular pentagon rather than the square.

The discovery of the Golden Section

In the first book of his work, *On the Philosophy of the Pythagoreans*[7], Iamblichus of Chalcis (ca. 283-330 A.D.) says that Hippasus, a student of Pythagoras, was the first to describe "the sphere made up of 12 pentagons. Because of this he perished at sea, an impious man." He is further said to have been "the first to betray the nature of commensurability and incommensurability to the unworthy." For these reasons, it is said, he was expelled from the Pythagorean order, and a grave was prepared for him, as though he were going to disappear completely from the circle of his previous companions.[8]

The anger of those who took the teachings of the Pythagoreans literally is understandable. By proving the existence of incommensurable segments, Hippasus had cast doubt on the fundamental theories of the Pythagoreans, and he had clearly not hesitated to pass the information on to "unworthy" men (that is, men who did not belong to the order).

Iamblichus tells us further that after the death of the Master, there was a split among the disciples of Pythagoras. The "acusmatics" ($\dot{\alpha}\kappa o \upsilon \sigma \mu \alpha \tau \iota \kappa o \acute{\iota}$) held to the "pure doctrine" and swore by the word of the Master. The "mathematicians," who, like Hippasus, were convinced of the existence of incommensurable segments, bent their efforts towards making further progress in mathematics. It is understandable that they were interested in exhibiting further pairs of incommensurable segments, and they soon discovered that the diagonal and side of a square have no common measure.

Today, the historians of mathematics tell us that at the time of Hippasus the Golden Section was not yet known. How, then, could he draw a regular pentagon at all, and use it to prove the incommensurability of a side and a diagonal? We can see the answer to the first question[9] in Figure 4. From the theorems on the sum of the interior angles in a triangle and the base angles of an isosceles triangle one can show that all the angles in this figure are

---

[7] A complete bibliography on the subject matter of this section can be found in Heller [I 9].

[8] A similar remark occurs in a scholium on Book 10 of Euclid (cf. [A 12], p. 8).

[9] We follow Heller [I 9].

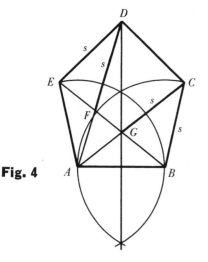

Fig. 4

multiples of 36°. From the converse of the theorem about the base angles of an isosceles triangle it is then clear that triangles EFD and CBG are isosceles, and hence $FD = ED = CG = CB = s$. This shows that we can construct the figure by means of a marked ruler. First draw the segment AB, then its perpendicular bisector, and then the circle with center B and radius AB. Now place a ruler, with two marks a distance s apart on it, so that it passes through A. If the first mark (starting from A) lies on the circle (at F), the second, lying on the perpendicular bisector, is the vertex D. In a similar way we find C and G. E is then determined by the circles about A and D with radius s.

Now a construction using a marked ruler is something different from one with ruler and compass, and it is to be assumed that the Pythagoreans were aware of this difference. Nevertheless, this construction provided them with a proof of the existence of a regular pentagon, and from this it is not hard to prove the existence of incommensurable segments. To do so we need only show that we can build on to an arbitrary regular pentagon P_1 an infinite sequence of smaller and smaller regular pentagons P_n. This can be done by making the shorter segment of a diagonal (CF in the first pentagon, P_1) the side of the pentagon. In Figure 5, $P_1(ABCDE)$, $P_2(BGHCF)$, $P_3(GKLHJ)$ and P_4 $(KNOLM)$ are shown.[10]

From the diagram the following relations between the sides s_n and the diagonals d_n of the pentagons can be read off:

(5) $$s_n = d_{n-1} - s_{n-1}, \qquad d_n = s_{n-1}.$$

Now if s_1 and d_1 had a common measure ϵ, we would have

$$s_1 = M_1 \cdot \epsilon, \qquad d_1 = N_1 \cdot \epsilon$$

where M_1 and N_1 are positive integers. From this and (5) it follows that

(6) $$s_2 = (N_1 - M_1) \cdot \epsilon = M_2 \cdot \epsilon, \qquad d_2 = M_1 \cdot \epsilon = N_2 \cdot \epsilon$$

---

[10] One obtains another sequence of pentagons $P_n{}^*$ which can be used in the same way by drawing all the diagonals of $P_1{}^*(=P_1)$ and thus getting a new, smaller pentagon, $P_2{}^*$. A repetition of this procedure gives a sequence of pentagons which are congruent to the odd-numbered pentagons of the first construction.

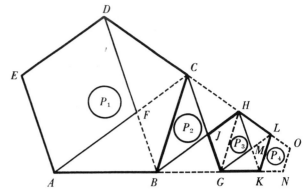

Fig. 5

with $M_2 < M_1$ and $N_2 < N_1$. A repetition of this argument shows that

$$M_{n+1} < M_n, \qquad N_{n+1} < N_n.$$

This must come to an end after a finite number of steps, since M_r and N_r are positive integers. On the other hand, the construction can be repeated indefinitely. Thus the assumption that the side and the diagonal of a regular pentagon have a common measure is false.

It is interesting to ask how the "mathematicians" among the followers of Pythagoras obtained the simple relation

(7) $$d(d - s) = s^2$$

between the diagonal d and the side s of a regular pentagon. This relation (7) is the basis for the construction of the Golden Section, today known to every student.

Heller [I 9] has suggested a very plausible hypothesis as to the path from the discoveries of Hippasus to (7). The "mathematicians" soon discovered that the side and the diagonal of a square were also incommensurable. This can be proved in a similar way, by constructing a sequence of smaller and smaller squares. If the square S_n has side s_n and diagonal d_n, we define S_{n+1} as the square with the side $d_n - s_n$. Then, as is easily seen[11], the following relations hold between the parts of the squares:

(8) $$s_{n+1} = d_n - s_n, \qquad d_{n+1} = s_n - s_{n+1}.$$

From (8) the incommensurability of the side and the diagonal of a square can be proved very easily. What is important to us here, however, is that the order of this construction can be reversed. If, in (8), we interchange n and $n + 1$, we get

(9) $$d_{n+1} = 2s_n + d_n, \qquad s_{n+1} = d_n + s_n.$$

In this way we can construct a sequence of larger and larger squares. Starting with an arbitrary square S_1^* of side s, and diagonal d, as "unit," we construct, following (9), the larger and larger squares $S_2^*, S_3^* \ldots .$

---

[11] See [A 12], p. 10.

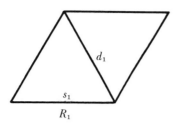 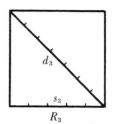

Fig. 6

The point of this is not obvious. But here we get a hint from the mystical philosophy of the Pythagoreans. According to Theon of Smyrna, the "unit," like a seed, carries in it all the characteristics of the future being. In our example it is able to generate the relation between the side and the diagonal of a square. "Just as the unit is at the beginning of everything, in the relation of the seed to the highest, so too the relation between the diagonal and the side is found in the unit."

Practically speaking, this means that one can construct a sequence of quadrilaterals in which the unit, that is to say the first quadrilateral, has *a diagonal equal to its side*. This seed is, therefore, not a square but a rhombus. Using (9) one can construct from this "unit" new rhombi which are more and more like a square. From (9) we can find the sides and diagonals of these rhombi. The table below gives the first few.

	s_n	d_n
R_1	1	1
R_2	2	3
R_3	5	7
R_4	12	17
R_5	29	41
...	...	...

Figure 6 shows the rhombi R_1 and R_3 in this sequence. One can easily show that the quotient d_n/s_n approaches $\sqrt{2}$.

From (9) it follows that

(10) $$2s_n^2 - d_n^2 = (-1)^{n+1} ;$$

hence, in modern notation,

$$\lim_{n \to \infty} d_n^2/s_n^2 = 2 .$$

In order to avoid repetition, we shall not prove (10), since a similar relation for pentagons will be derived below.[12]

---

[12] The proof of (10), which was already known to Theon of Smyrna, may be found, for example, in van der Waerden [I 6], p. 126.

The Pythagoreans

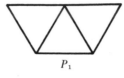

P_1

Fig. 7

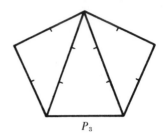

P_3

According to an illuminating conjecture of Heller [I 9], the Pythagoreans may have discovered the Golden Section by means of a similar argument about a sequence of pentagons. In the proof of the incommensurability of the side and the diagonal of a pentagon we used a sequence of smaller and smaller pentagons. Let us, as we did in the case of a square, reverse the order of construction of the pentagons. Interchanging n and $n-1$ in (5) gives

$$(11) \qquad d_n = s_{n-1} + d_{n-1}, \qquad s_n = d_{n-1}$$

which is the law of construction for an infinite sequence of pentagons with increasing sides and diagonals.

Here too we can take as "seed" or "unit" a pentagon with $s = d = 1$. Then from (11) we get for the sides and diagonals of the sequence [13] of (nonregular) pentagons the following results:

s_n	1	1	2	3	5	8	13	21	$\cdots$
d_n	1	2	3	5	8	13	21	34	$\cdots$

Figure 7 shows the pentagons P_1, P_3, and P_6. In this case, too, intuition tells us that with increasing n the pentagons get more and more "like" a regular pentagon. In order to replace this vague formulation with a precise statement, we deduce from (11) the relation

$$(12) \qquad d_n(d_n - s_n) - s_n^2 = (-1)^n .$$

This can be expressed in words as follows: if the side s_n is laid off on the diagonal d_n of the pentagon P_n of our sequence, the diagonal is divided into segments such that the rectangle whose sides are the diagonal d_n and the shorter of the two segments has an area which is alternately one larger and one smaller than the square on the longer segment s_n. This is easily proved by mathematical induction. Clearly, (12) is true for $n = 1$, since then $d_1 = s_1 = 1$. Suppose it holds for $n = k - 1$; that is, suppose

$$(13) \qquad d_{k-1}(d_{k-1} - s_{k-1}) - s_{k-1}^2 = (-1)^{k-1} .$$

---

[13] The sequence $\{s_n\}$ is the well-known Fibonacci sequence $\{\text{Fib }(n)\}$, which is defined by the difference equation
$$\text{Fib }(n+1) = \text{Fib }(n) + \text{Fib }(n-1)$$
and the initial conditions Fib $(1) = $ Fib $(2) = 1$. Then $d_n = $ Fib $(n+1)$, which follows at once from (11). For the properties of this sequence see, for example, [I 10], p. 17.

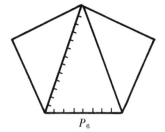

P_6

From (13) and (11) it follows that

$$s_k^2 - s_k(d_k - s_k) - (d_k - s_k)^2 = (-1)^{k-1}$$

or

$$d_k(d_k - s_k) - s_k^2 = (-1)^k .$$

Thus (12) holds for every natural number n.

We have used here[14] the principle of mathematical induction. Can we assume it was already known to the Pythagoreans? It is often claimed that Pascal[15] was the first to use this method of proof. According to van der Waerden ([I 6], p. 126), however, the Pythagoreans had actually proved (10) by a method one can call induction. Thus it is possible that a similar procedure was used in obtaining the Golden Section. From equation (10) one can deduce the relation $d^2 = 2s^2$ for the square. Thus from (12) it is an easy step to conjecture that (7) holds for a regular pentagon.

Equation (7) has the following geometric meaning: in a regular pentagon, if a side is laid off along a diagonal, the diagonal is divided into two segments such that the area of a rectangle whose sides are the diagonal and the diagonal less the side equals the area of a square on the side of the pentagon. This division, known today to every high school student as the Golden Section, should not have proved hard for the "mathematicians" among the disciples of Pythagoras to carry out correctly with ruler and compass. Heller points out that similar constructions were often performed at that time. Everything depended, therefore, on discovering the truth of (7).

So far, we have only made the conjecture that (7) holds, plausible. Now, however, a complete proof presents no difficulties. It is easily shown (the theorem is to be found in Euclid, IV 10) that an isosceles triangle whose base equals the longer segment of a leg divided in the Golden Section has the property characteristic of $\triangle ACD$ (Figure 4) in the regular pentagon: the base angles are twice as big as the vertex angle.

Archimedes once said that the man who first states a theorem deserves as much credit as the man who first proves it. This thesis is confirmed by the history of the Golden Section. In this case the real difficulty lay in discovering (7). Once this conjecture was made, it was not hard to prove.

---

[14] Heller avoids the induction step.
[15] See Chap. IV.

Archimedes

*There are things which seem incredible to most men
who have not studied mathematics.*

Archimedes

The uses of mathematics

Plutarch reports that Plato scorned such mathematicians as Eudoxus and Archytas, who used mathematics to solve problems in mechanics. He accused them of "lowering the dignity of geometry by letting it sink from the immaterial and intellectual to the material." To him the study of geometry was the best road to the world of ideas. One did not use this science to earn money[16]. Nor did one demean it by applying it to technical problems.

What kind of mathematics was done in Plato's Academy can still be learned from the most famous textbook in the history of the world.[17] The 13 parts of the *Elements*, compiled by Euclid about 300 B.C., make it clear that the mathematicians of that era already knew how to use methods which can be called exact even by today's standards.[18] Every effort was made not to rely on the unsupported intuition but to construct geometry as a scientific system with a precise axiomatic foundation. There was no room for applications to technical problems.

A new relationship between mathematics and technology was brought about by Archimedes of Syracuse (about 287-212 B.C.). He can be called the spiritual father of our modern institutes of technology. However, Plutarch reports that he, too, considered "mechanical work and every art concerned with the necessities of life an ignoble and inferior form of labor and therefore exerted his best efforts only in seeking knowledge of those things in which the good and the beautiful were not mixed with the necessary."

Nevertheless, it is known that Archimedes became remarkably skilled at this "ignoble" work. He used a compound pulley to draw freighters to shore effortlessly, and for King Hieron he constructed siege machines and other technical wonder-weapons. We shall not give any further details of this aspect of his activities[19]. What interests us is his mathematical work, particularly the way he solved mathematical problems by reasoning about physical things.

First let us note that Archimedes did not give up the sort of rigor in his proofs that had been usual in Greek mathematics until then. Quite the

---

[16] It is reported that when a student asked Euclid what geometry could be used for, Euclid told a slave to give the young man a few gold pieces, since he felt he must profit from his knowledge.

[17] It is the only textbook in common use for over 2000 years.

[18] This is not to deny that today we must describe Euclid's system of axioms as incomplete. In this connection see [A 12], p. 15 ff.

[19] See, for example, [A 4], [II 3].

contrary! His proofs in the field of stereometry, for example, are of an exemplary clarity, and one can only wish the reasoning in modern school mathematics were as precise as that of Archimedes. The proofs in his writings on "Sphere and Cylinder" are so complete that time after time one says to himself: "Beautiful, but how did he hit on it?"[20]

Luckily we are in a position to answer this question, thanks to the discovery by Heiberg in 1906 of the Constantinople manuscript. We now have a letter from Archimedes to Eratosthenes which answers a number of riddles for us. Archimedes often attained insights into geometric relationships by means of mechanical considerations. He himself writes on this subject:

> Certain theorems first became clear to me by means of a mechanical method. Then, however, they had to be proved geometrically since the method provided no real proof. It is obviously easier to find a proof when we have already learned something about the question by means of the method than it is to find one without such advance knowledge. That is why, for example, we must give Democritus, who was the first to state the theorems that the cone is a third of the cylinder and the pyramid of the prism, but who did not prove them, as much credit as we give to Eudoxus, who was the first to prove them.

We will give two examples of the reasoning of the great geometer:

a) the (rigorous geometric) proof of the theorem about the area of a spherical surface, and
b) the "heuristic" method of finding the volume of a sphere.

Nowadays in the schools, the formula for the area of the surface of a sphere is usually derived by means of a shorter procedure. For that very reason it is worthwhile to study the rigorous but somewhat detailed method that Archimedes used. His research on stereometry did much to prepare the way for the integral calculus.

---

[20] Schopenhauer called such mathematical deductions "mouse-trap proofs."

The surface of a sphere

We now give (in modern terminology) Archimedes' proof of the theorem on the area of a sphere.

Theorem 1. The area of a sphere is four times that of its greatest circle.

To prove this we make use of the following auxiliary theorem:

Theorem 2. If, for the segments x_i and y_i ($i = 1, 2, 3, \ldots, m$), the equation[21]

$$(1) \qquad x_1/y_1 = x_2/y_2 = \cdots = x_m/y_m$$

holds, then

$$(2) \qquad x_1 \sum_{i=2}^{m} y_i = y_1 \sum_{i=2}^{m} x_i .$$

For from (1) it follows that $x_1 y_i = y_1 x_i$ for $i = 2, 3, \ldots, m$, and by summing we get (2) at once.

To prove Theorem 1, Archimedes also used some properties of a cone and a frustrum of a cone which we shall assume known:[22]

Theorem 3. The lateral area of an isosceles cone is equal to that of a circle whose radius is the mean proportional between the slant height of the cone and the radius of the base.

Theorem 4. The lateral area of a frustrum of a cone with radii r_1 and r_2 and slant height s is equal to the area of a circle whose radius is the mean proportioned between s and $r_1 + r_2$.

The next step in the proof of Theorem 1 is:

Theorem 5. Let P be a regular 4n-sided polygon with vertices A, A_1, A_2, $\ldots$, A_{2n}, A_{2n-1}', $\ldots$, A_2', A_1' inscribed in a circle of radius r. Let V be the solid of revolution generated by rotating P about the axis AA_{2n}. Then the area of the surface of V is smaller than four times the area of the circle.

---

[21] One must remember that in Archimedes' works, proportions, equations and inequalities must always be interpreted geometrically. They are *not* statements about real numbers associated with the geometric objects.

[22] There is a proof of these theorems in [II 1]. Using modern methods they can be deduced easily from known formulas for volumes.

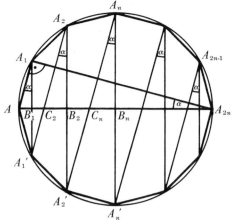

Fig. 8

Proof: Draw the diagonals AA_{2n}, A_1A_1', A_2A_2', ..., A_2A_1, A_3A_2', ..., A_1A_{2n} of the polygon Figure 8. Let $B_i(C_i)$ be the intersection of $A_iA_i'(A_iA_{i-1}')$ and AA_{2n}. Then the segments A_1A_1', ..., $A_{2n-1}A_{2n-1}'$ are perpendicular to AA_{2n} and the diagonals A_2A_1', A_3A_2', ..., $A_{2n}A_{2n-1}'$ are parallel in pairs.[23] It follows that

$$(3) \qquad \frac{A_1A_{2n}}{AA_1} = \frac{A_1B_1}{AB_1} = \frac{A_1'B_1}{B_1C_2} = \cdots = \frac{A_{2n-1}B_{2n-1}}{B_{2n-1}C_{2n-1}} = \frac{A_{2n-1}'B_{2n-1}}{B_{2n-1}A_{2n}}$$

From (3) and Theorem 2 it follows that

$$(4) \qquad AA_1(A_1A_1' + A_2A_2' + \cdots + A_{2n-1}A_{2n-1}') = A_1A_{2n} \cdot AA_{2n}.$$

We shall use this relation (4) to estimate the surface area of the solid of revolution V.

This solid V is made up of 2 cones and $2n - 2$ frustra of cones. With each of these pieces let us associate a circle whose area is equal to that of the lateral surface of the cone or frustrum of a cone. By Theorems 3 and 4 the sum of the squares of the radii of these $2n$ circles is

$$(5) \qquad \sum_{i=1}^{2n} r_i^2 = AA_1 \cdot A_1B_1 + A_1A_2(A_1B_1 + A_2B_2) + \cdots$$
$$+ A_{2n-2}A_{2n-1}(A_{2n-2}B_{2n-2} + A_{2n-1}B_{2n-1})$$
$$+ A_{2n-1}A_{2n} \cdot A_{2n-1}.$$

In view of $AA_1 = A_1A_2 = \cdots = A_{2n-1}A_{2n}$, $2A_iB_i = A_iA_i'$ ($i = 1, 2, \ldots, 2n - 1$) and (4), the sum of the squares of the radii can also be written

$$(6) \qquad \sum_{i=1}^{2n} r_i^2 = AA_1(A_1A_1' + \cdots + A_{2n-1}A_{2n-1}') = A_1A_{2n} \cdot AA_{2n}.$$

If R is the radius of a circle whose area is equal to that of the surface of the solid of revolution, then from (6) it follows that

---

[23] The angles marked α in Figure 8 are peripheral angles subtending equal arcs.

$$R^2 = \sum_{i=1}^{2n} r_i^2 = A_1 A_{2n} \cdot A A_{2n} .$$

Since

$$A_1 A_{2n} < A A_{2n}$$

it follows that

$$R^2 < (A A_{2n})^2 = 4r^2 , \text{q.e.d.}$$

Correspondingly we have for the circumscribed regular polygon with $4n$ sides:

Theorem 6. Let P^* be a regular polygon of $4n$ sides, with vertices A^*, A_1^*, $A_2^*, \ldots, A_{2n}^*$, $A_{2n-1}'^*, \ldots, A_2'^*$, $A_1'^*$ circumscribed about a circle of radius r^*. Let V^* be the solid of revolution generated by rotating P^* about the axis $A^* A_{2n}^*$. Then the area of the surface of V^* is greater than four times the area of the circle (Figure 9).

The regular polygon P^* circumscribed about the circle is *inscribed* in a certain larger circle. By (7), therefore, if R^* is the radius of the circle whose area is equal to that of the surface of V^*,

(9) $$R^{*2} = A_1^* A_{2n}^* \cdot A^* A_{2n}^* .$$

But (Figure 9)

$$A_1^* A_{2n}^* = 2 D_1 B_n = 2r^*$$

and so by (9)

$$R^{*2} > A_1^* A_{2n}^{*2} = 4r^{*2}, \text{q.e.d.}$$

From our results we deduce also

Theorem 7. The areas of the surfaces of the inscribed and circumscribed solids of revolution V and V^* are to each other as the squares of their sides.

Proof: From (7) and (9) and the similarity of the triangles $A A_1 A_{2n}$ and $A^* A_1^* A_{2n}^*$ it follows that

(11) $$\frac{S(V)}{S(V^*)} = \frac{R^2}{R^{*2}} = \frac{A_1 A_{2n} \cdot A A_{2n}}{A_1^* A_{2n}^* \cdot A^* A_{2n}^*} = \frac{A A_1^2}{A^* A_1^{*2}} .$$

Finally, to prove Theorem 1 we also need

Theorem 8. The area of the surface of the inscribed solid of revolution V is smaller, and the area of the surface of the circumscribed solid of revolution V^* is larger, than that of the sphere.

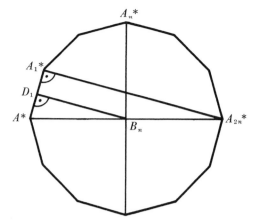

Fig. 9

This theorem is an immediate consequence of the following assumption, which Archimedes made the axiomatic foundation of his reasoning ([II 1], p. 4):

> Of other surfaces with the same extremities, the extremities being in a plane, [any two] such are unequal whenever both are concave in the same direction and one surface is either wholly included between the other and the plane which has the same extremities with it, or is partly included by, and partly common with, the other; and that [surface] which is included is the lesser [of the two in area].

Of course, it is an obvious question whether this assumption cannot be deduced from simpler axioms. However, we shall follow Archimedes' argument and thus accept Theorem 8 on the basis of his assumption.

We can now proceed with the proof of Theorem 1. Archimedes uses an indirect argument similar to many others we find in his writings.[24] Let S be the given sphere, with radius r, C a circle with radius $2r$.

(*Assumption I*). *Let us assume that the area of C, $A(C)$, is smaller than the surface area $A(S)$ of the sphere.*

Then there exist segments of lengths b and c ($b > c$) such that

$$(12) \qquad\qquad b/c < \frac{A(S)}{A(C)}.$$

Let d be the mean proportional between b and c, so that $bc = d^2$. Given a great circle of S, construct the circumscribed and inscribed regular polygons of $4n$ sides referred to in Theorems 6 and 5. Make the number of vertices $(4n)$ so large that the ratio of the sides of these polygons ($A^*A_1^*/AA_1$ in Figures 8 and 9) is smaller than b/d.[25] Rotating these polygons about the axis AA_{2n}

---

[24] For example, the area of a circle and the volume of a sphere are determined in a similar way.

[25] We omit the proof that such an approximation exists. It is given in Archimedes [II 1], p. 6, Theorem 3.

generates once more the solids of revolution V and V^* referred to in Theorems 5 and 6, respectively. From Theorem 7 and equation (12) it follows that

(13) $$\frac{A(V^*)}{A(V)} = \frac{A^*A_1^{*2}}{AA_1^*} < \frac{b^2}{d^2} = \frac{b}{c} < \frac{A(S)}{A(C)}.$$

But by Theorems 5 and 8

(14) $$\frac{A(V^*)}{A(V)} > \frac{A(S)}{A(C)}.$$

Since inequalities (13) and (14) are inconsistent, Assumption I is false.

(Assumption II). Now assume that $A(C) > A(S)$.

Then pick two segments of lengths b and c such that

(15) $$b/c = \frac{A(C)}{A(S)}.$$

As before, let d be the mean proportional between b and c. Then by an argument similar to that used above, we get

(16) $$\frac{A(V^*)}{A(V)} < \frac{A(C)}{A(S)}.$$

But by Theorems 6 and 8,

(17) $$\frac{A(V^*)}{A(V)} > \frac{A(C)}{A(S)}.$$

Since (16) and (17) are inconsistent, Assumption II is also false. The only remaining possibility is that $A(C) = A(S)$, as Theorem 1 asserts.

Using a similar procedure Archimedes proves

Theorem 9. The area of a sphere is four times that of a cone whose base is equal in area to a great circle of the sphere and whose altitude is equal to the radius of the sphere.

A heuristic argument

The rather complicated method of proof found in Archimedes' investigations of volumes gives no hint as to how he discovered the theorems to be proved. From his letter to Eratosthenes we know, for example, that he found the

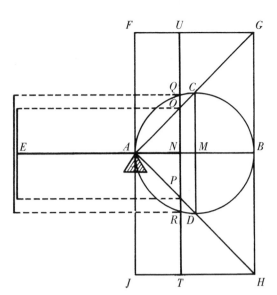

Fig. 10

volume of a sphere by an argument using infinitesimals, in which a sphere is considered a sum of circular discs. Thus he anticipated the later "method of indivisibles." It must be emphasized, however, that Archimedes considered the procedure an aid to discovering theorems, not a valid method of proof.

The proof of Theorem 9 then goes as follows:

Let AB and CD be a pair of perpendicular diameters of a great circle G of the given sphere S. Let r be the radius of S, M its center (Figure 10).

Then ACD is a cross section of the cone of Theorem 9. Also shown in Figure 10 is a cross section $FGHJ$ of a right cylinder with axis AB and radius of base $AF = AB$. Let UT be an arbitrary·parallel to CD, meeting AB in N (between A and M), the circle G in Q and R, and the cross section of the cone in O and P.

In the following we shall denote a circle with radius $r = MC$ by $K(r)$ or $K(MC)$, a square with side a by $S(a)$, and finally a rectangle with sides a and b by $R(a, b)$. Then from Figure 10 we can read off the following equations:

$$\begin{aligned} S(ON) + S(NQ) &= S(AN) + S(NQ) \\ &= S(AQ) \\ &= R(AN, AB) \\ &= R(ON, NU) . \end{aligned}$$

From these follow the proportions

$$\frac{S(ON) + S(NQ)}{S(NU)} = \frac{R(ON, NU)}{S(NU)} = \frac{ON}{NU}$$

and correspondingly,

(18)
$$\frac{K(ON) + K(NQ)}{K(NU)} = \frac{ON}{NU} .$$

21

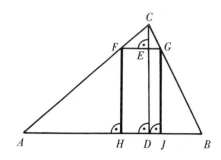

Fig. 11

Now think of the axis AB extended beyond A a distance equal to AB. Then we can picture this axis as the arm of a balance, supported at A. We leave the cross section $K(NU)$ of the cylinder where it is, but hang the two circles $K(ON)$ and $K(NQ)$ at E. Then $K(ON) + K(NQ)$ represents the weight hanging at E, $K(NU)$ the weight hanging at N. By (18) the cross section of the cylinder (hanging at N) and the cross sections of the cone and the sphere (hanging at E) are in equilibrium.

Now let this displacement of the cross sections of the cone and sphere be carried out for every intersection UT between A and B. Then we have a state of equilibrium for a lever, with the whole cone (of cross section AHG) and the whole sphere hanging at the point E. The cylinder remains in its place. From symmetry it is clear that M is the center of gravity, and hence by the principle of levers

$$(19) \qquad \text{cone } (AHG) + \text{sphere} = \tfrac{1}{2} \text{ cylinder,}$$

since the lever arm AM is just half as long as the lever arm AE.
Also, since

$$\text{cone } (ACD) = (\tfrac{1}{8}) \text{ cone } (AGH)$$

and

$$\text{cylinder} = 3 \text{ cone } (AGH)$$

it follows from (19) that

$$\text{sphere} = 4 \text{ cone } (ACD) \text{ , q.e.d.}$$

This argument may appeal to the reader and he may not see why this fairly short derivation is not a valid proof. Archimedes himself did not consider the argument incomplete because it used the principle of levers. In "The Quadrature of the Parabola," which was published officially during his lifetime, he made use of theorems on centers of gravity. Theoretical mechanics, after all, can be developed axiomatically just as precisely as "pure" mathematics.

The criticisms of the type of reasoning employed above are directed against the "indivisibles," that is, against the division of a solid figure into an infinite number of infinitely thin slices. Figure 11 shows that careless use of this procedure can lead to false conclusions. In triangle ABC, let $AC > BC$.

Then the triangle $ACD(CD \perp AB)$ is certainly larger than the triangle CBD. On the other hand, every parallel FG to AB associates with the perpendicular FH to AB exactly one equally long perpendicular GJ. The correspondence is one-to-one and every interior point of the two sub-triangles is on just one perpendicular. In this way each subtriangle can be dissected into infinitely many perpendiculars, and the two sets of perpendiculars can be put into one-to-one correspondence in such a way that corresponding ones have equal lengths. Nevertheless, it would be wrong to assert that the two figures have the same area.

This example[26] shows that care is required in the use of infinitesimal methods. Archimedes only used this argument involving a lever to discover relationships between the sphere and the cylinder and between the sphere and the cone at first only conjectured to hold. The proofs of the conjectures then followed along the lines indicated in the second section of this chapter.

---

[26] Example not due to Archimedes.

Nicholas of Cusa

*If we can approach the Divine only through symbols,
then it is most suitable that we use mathematical
symbols, for these have an indestructible certainty.*

Nicholas of Cusa ([III 2], p. 90)

On informed ignorance

In the first centuries of the Christian era, mathematics was not in a flourishing state. It was suspect because of its close connection with heathen philosophy. Many even considered it the work of the devil, since the soothsayers and astrologers often called themselves mathematicians.

Towards the end of the Middle Ages, however, this changed, at least among the theologians, who were schooled in philosophy. As the interest in the ideas of the ancient world grew, so did the tendency to use mathematical pictures and symbols in philosophical and theological reasoning. There were even thinkers who were seriously concerned with advancing mathematical knowledge.

The most important among the mathematicians of this era was the German cardinal, Nicholas of Cusa (1401-1464). Admittedly, measured by modern standards his accomplishments in the field are not exciting. He got no further than Archimedes with the problem of squaring the circle. Furthermore, today we must reject some of his deductions as incorrect. Nevertheless, we must rate him as one of the great thinkers who learned much from mathematics, because his work in that field made him aware of both the possibilities and the limitations of all human thought.

He says that mathematical entities are "of the highest constancy and certainty."

> Thus wise men have been right in taking examples of things which can be investigated with the mind from the field of mathematics, and not one of the ancients who is considered of real importance approached a difficult problem except by way of a mathematical analogy. That is why Boethius, the greatest scholar among the Romans, said that for a man entirely unversed in mathematics, knowledge of the Divine was unattainable.

This statement is taken from the book *On Informed Ignorance* (*De docta ignorantia*). The ideas in this work about the meaning of numbers are related to those of Plato and the Pythagoreans, but he reaches conclusions not found among the mathematicians of antiquity. For Plato, the path from a mathematical deduction to a metaphysical speculation is very short.[27] Cusanus

---

[27] See, for example, [A 12], Chapter II.

also uses mathematical pictures and symbols to clarify theological and philosophical statements, but mathematical reflections always lead him to critical observations on the limitations of all human knowledge. The problems about infinitesimals make him realize how uncertain many metaphysical arguments are. His goal, therefore, is to achieve a state of "informed ignorance" ([III 2], p. 75).

> If we fully achieve this, we shall have attained to a state of informed ignorance. For even he who is most greedy for knowledge can achieve no greater perfection than to be thoroughly aware of his own ignorance in his particular field. The more he knows, the more aware he will be of his ignorance. It is for this reason that I have taken the trouble to write a little about informed ignorance.

He came to hold this critical point of view regarding all human knowledge through his work on squaring the circle ([III 2], p. 78).

> The finite mind can therefore not attain to the full truth about things through similarity. For the truth is neither more nor less, but rather indivisible. What is itself not true can no more measure the truth than what is not a circle can measure a circle, whose being is indivisible. Hence reason, which is not the truth, can never grasp the truth so exactly that it could not be grasped infinitely more exactly. Reason stands in the same relation to the truth as the polygon to the circle: the more vertices a polygon has, the more it resembles a circle; yet even when the number of vertices grows infinite, the polygon never becomes equal to a circle, unless it becomes a circle in its true nature.
>
> The real nature of what exists, which constitutes its truth, is therefore never entirely attainable. It has been sought by all the philosophers, but never really found. The further we penetrate into informed ignorance, the closer we come to the truth itself.

Similar insights have been reached by modern thinkers (though for different reasons) through investigation of the foundations of mathematics.[28] By comparison, Cusanus' purely technical achievements in mathematics were modest.

---

[28] See, for example, Stegmüller's *Metaphysik, Wissenschaft, Skepsis*, Frankfort on the Main — Vienna, 1954, or [A 12], Chapter XIII.

He advanced only slightly beyond the point Archimedes had reached in the problem of finding the area and the circumference of a circle.

Squaring the circle

Cusanus devoted many papers to the classical problem of squaring the circle.[29] In other words, he tried to construct, with ruler and compass, a side of a square equal in area to a given circle. This is related to the problem of rectification: to find a segment whose length is equal to the circumference of a given circle.

Nicholas of Cusa gave many solutions which he believed could not be improved on. Nevertheless, he said again and again that the quadrature problem could not be solved, because "the area of a circle is incommensurable with that of any non-circle" ([III 1], p. 51).

There seems to be a contradiction here. We see how Cusanus avoids it in a passage from his paper "De circuli quadratura" ([III 1], p. 41):

> Those who hold firmly to the first view[30] seem to be satisfied with the fact that given a circle, there exists a square which is neither larger nor smaller than the circle. ... If, however, this square is neither smaller nor larger than the circle, by even the smallest assignable fraction, they call it equal. For this is how they understand equality — one thing is equal to another if it neither exceeds it nor falls short of it by any rational fraction, even the smallest. *If one understands the notion of equality in this way, then, I believe, one can correctly say that, given the circumference of a certain polygon, there exists a circle with the same circumference.*[31] If, however, one interprets the idea of equality, insofar as it applies to a quantity, absolutely and without regard to rational fractions, then the statement of the others is right: *there is no noncircular area which is precisely equal to a circular area.*

J. E. Hofmann has given the following interpretation of Cusanus' position ([III 1], p. 206): he considers it possible to construct a segment which is equal to the circumference of the circle "to within an infinitesimal quantity." The

---

[29] They are all contained in the volume [III 1].
[30] This refers to the view that the quadrature problem is solvable.
[31] Italics added by Meschkowski.

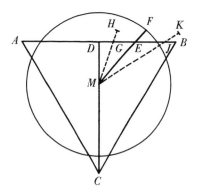

Fig. 12

error, which cannot be eliminated, is thus, according to this view, smaller than any rational fraction of unity. It seems possible to us that Hofmann's interpretation attributes to Cusanus a way of thinking which first became usual among the founders of the infinitesimal calculus. Our cardinal is quite convinced that he can construct a segment which is neither smaller nor larger than the circumference of the circle. He simply does not venture to use the word "equal" because by doing so he would deny the differences between a circle and a line. The circle is not merely a polygon with "very" many vertices, and thus the circumference of a circle and a segment are simply "incommensurable." A corresponding statement holds true, of course, for the quadrature problem.

However, no matter how they are interpreted, Cusanus' views on the possibility of the construction are simply false. All the procedures he gives are approximate constructions and one can always find ordinary rational bounds for the error, which exists in each. Archimedes knew that the value $22\frac{2}{7}$ which he gave for the ratio of the circumference to the diameter of a circle was an approximation. Cusanus succeeded, more than 16 centuries later, in getting a little better estimate of this ratio. But he was wrong in thinking his procedure could not be improved upon.

We shall restrict ourselves to presenting the most accurate of his constructions.

In Figure 12, ABC is an equilateral triangle with altitude CD and circumcenter M. We are to find the radius of a circle with the same circumference as triangle ABC. To accomplish this, bisect BD at E and extend ME beyond E by an amount $\frac{1}{4} ME$. Then $MF = \frac{5}{4} ME$ is the desired radius.

To establish this construction the cardinal says:

> So you will not think that this is mere conjecture, that one is not led to this claim by any other line of thought, you can draw a rigorous conclusion, which in this case is completely accurate and is dependable to within the smallest rational fraction. Draw through[32] M a line to a

---

[32] The points are labeled here as they were in Figure 12.

point near D, say G, and extend it in the ratio DG/AB. Then the new segment[33] is shorter than the one we are seeking. If we extend it in the ratio GB/AB, then it is also shorter than the one we are seeking. If we draw through M another line to a point near B, say J, and extend it in the ratio JB/AB, the new segment is longer than the one we are seeking. If we extend it in the ratio DJ/AB, it is also longer, as we can see. Thus we can draw through M towards DB a segment which is neither longer nor shorter than the desired one, by extending it in the ratio between the segment from its endpoint to D, and the segment AB.

The modern mathematician needs no proof that this argument is not valid. Clearly Cusanus has been guided by the intuitively obvious fact that for points "near D" this construction gives a value of the desired radius which is too small, for points "near B" one which is too large. This does not mean, of course, that the midpoint E gives the right value. Nevertheless, his construction gives an approximation to the number π which is a little better than that of Archimedes.

The ratio of the circumference of a circle to its diameter, later called π, is, according to Cusanus,

$$(1) \qquad \pi_c = \frac{6 \cdot \sqrt{2700}}{\frac{5}{2} \cdot \sqrt{1575}} = \frac{24}{35} \sqrt{21} \; .$$

In fact, if we substitute the number 60, for the radius r of the circumscribed circle we get

$$DM = \tfrac{1}{3}DC = \tfrac{1}{2}MC = (\tfrac{1}{2})r = 30$$
$$DB = \sqrt{2700} \; .$$

The perimeter P of the triangle T and (it is claimed) of the circle O of equal perimeter with center M and radius MF, is, then

$$P = 6 \cdot \sqrt{2700} \; .$$

But the diameter of O is $2MF = \frac{5}{2} \sqrt{1575}$. This gives for π the approximate value

$$(2) \qquad \pi_c = \frac{24}{35} \sqrt{21} = 3.142337 \ldots \ldots$$

---

[33] MH in Figure 12.

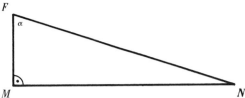

Fig. 13

This is only slightly better than Archimedes' value

(3) $$\pi_A = 22\tfrac{2}{7} = 3.142857\ldots.$$

There is still an error of

(4) $$\pi_c - \pi = 3.142337\ldots - 3.1415926\ldots = 0.00074\ldots > 7 \cdot 10^{-4}.$$

Thus Cusanus is wrong in thinking that by his construction the error can be made smaller than "a rational fraction."

His later attempts did not improve this approximation to π. It is interesting, however, to see what he considers a "practical" solution of the converse problem, that is, the rectification of a given circle.

The construction shown in Figure 12 gives the radius of a circle whose circumference is approximately equal to a given segment. This segment is three times the side AB of the given triangle (Figure 12). Figure 13 shows the circle with radius MF of Figure 12, and a segment MN (perpendicular to MF) equal to half the perimeter of the equilateral triangle ABC: $MN = \tfrac{3}{2}AB$. If we draw the corresponding figure for another radius MF', we get a triangle $MF'N'$ similar to triangle MFN. The angle $\alpha = \angle\, MFN$ (= arc tan π) is thus independent of the radius of the circle.

Cusanus uses this fact to solve the "converse problem." He says to construct the angle α "of brass or wood."

> If you want to straighten out a circular arc, draw through the center a line of indefinite length which makes a right angle with the diameter. Then lay the angle on the intersection of the diameter and the circumference so that the shorter side lies along the diameter. Then, on the line of indefinite length, the longer side of the angle cuts off a segment equal to half the circumference of the circle ([III 1], pp. 86-87).

Of course, this is not a "ruler and compass" construction, but it is a thoroughly practical way of solving the rectification problem.

Blaise Pascal

The mathematicians who are merely mathematicians reason correctly, but only when everything has been explained to them in terms of definitions and principles. Otherwise they are limited and insufferable, for they only reason correctly when they are dealing with very clear principles.

Pascal ([IV 1], p. 53)

The course of a prodigy

Gilberte Pascal-Périer, the sister of the mathematician, says[34] of the unique educational methods of their father, Etienne Pascal, that because he knew "mathematics fills and satisfies the soul, he did not want my brother to learn anything about it, so that he would not neglect Latin and the other languages." However, it did not help. In his hours of recreation, Blaise Pascal (1623-1662) dreamt in geometric figures; he drew circles and triangles with chalk on the flagstones of the floor.

> But since my father had been so careful to conceal all these things from him that he did not even know their names, he was forced to invent his own names. Thus he called a circle a "round," a line a "rod," and similarly for all the rest. Using these names, he set up axioms and finally complete proofs. And since, in these matters, one proceeds from one thing to another, he continued to make progress and pushed his investigations to the point where he reached the 32nd proposition of Book 1 of Euclid. And just as he was occupied with this, my father happened to enter the room in which he was working, without my brother's hearing him. He found my brother so busy that for some time he was not aware of my father's entrance. It is impossible to say who was the more surprised: the son when he saw his father and thought of the explicit prohibition the latter had uttered, or the father, when he found his son thus occupied. The astonishment of the father was even greater, however, when he asked his son what he was doing and the latter answered that he was investigating a certain matter — which turned out to be Proposition 32 of Book I of Euclid.[35] My father was so shocked by the greatness and ability of this genius that he left him without saying a word.

In this way the twelve year old, if one can believe his sister's account, discovered substantial parts of geometry for himself. Now his father let him read Euclid's *Elements*.

---

[34] *The Life of Blaise Pascal*, by his sister, Gilberte Pascal-Périer. Included in [IV 1] and [IV 2]; quoted here from [IV 1], p. XXX ff.
[35] This is the theorem about the sum of the interior angles of a triangle.

He used only his hours of recreation on this study, since he was learning Latin according to the rules my father had laid down for him. Since, however, he found in this science the truth, which he had always so passionately sought, it satisfied him so completely that he threw his whole soul into the work. Thus no matter how little time he had left for it, he made such strides that at the age of sixteen he wrote a paper on the conic sections[36] which was considered such an important intellectual achievement that it was said nothing so powerful had been seen since Archimedes.

In his later years, however, Pascal turned almost entirely away from mathematics. Gilberte reports:

When he was not yet twenty-four years old,[37] Divine Providence induced him to read pious books, and God enlightened him so much by this reading of holy works that he saw clearly that the Christian religion requires us to live only for God and to have no other goal but Him. And this truth seemed to him so enlightening, so necessary and so useful, that it put an end to all his investigations. ([IV 1], p. XXXV.)

And thus Pascal became the uncompromising religious thinker, the author of *Lettres à un Provincial* and of the *Pensées*, which is still often read. It is not our job to assess Pascal's religious writings. We shall concern ourselves with the mathematician Pascal.

Although the young thinker, plagued by constant pain from his eighteenth year,[38] devoted only a few years of his short life to the exact sciences, it is difficult to choose a few typical examples from his many-sided works. Pascal was not merely a geometer. He also discovered new results in arithmetic and probability theory. And his work on infinitesimal problems later led Leibnitz to use the "characteristic triangle" to solve the tangent problem.[39] Finally, he also designed a calculating machine and busied himself with problems of mathematical physics.

---

[36] This work has not come down to us.
[37] In the opinion of modern scholars, Gilberte Pascal-Périer's chronology is not dependable.
[38] See [IV, 1], p. XXXIV.
[39] See Chapter V.

We shall give an account of his method of "mathematical induction" and of his ideas on the use of axioms in mathematics, which he described in his *Methods and Psychology of the Scholar*.

The principle of mathematical induction

Nowadays, if we want to prove a theorem concerning the natural numbers, we often use the "principle of mathematical induction": if a statement $A(n)$ holds when $n = 1$, and if, from the truth of the statement for any natural number n, it follows that the statement is also true for $n + 1$, then the statement $A(n)$ is true for every natural number.

In the language of a formal calculus, this can be expressed as follows:

$$A(\,|\,); \qquad A(n) \to A(n\,|\,) \vdash_{K} A(n) \ .$$

Here K is any formal calculus which contains the "atom" $|$ and the rule $a \to a|$.[40]

Every first term college student knows simple examples of the use of this principle.[41] In the opinion of some historians of mathematics[42], it was already known by the Pythagoreans, but it became accessible to modern mathematicians through the work of Pascal. He first used it in his *Traité du Triangle Arithmétique*.

Figure 14 shows "Pascal's triangle" in the form Pascal himself used in his writings. Ten rows, each of $11 - n(n = 1, 2, \ldots, 10)$ numbered squares, are arranged so that the squares with the same number in different rows lie in a vertical column.

Today we would use double subscripts for such a system of squares (or "cells"):

$$\{q_{mn}\} \ , \text{ where } m = 1, 2, \ldots, N,$$
$$n = 1, 2, \ldots, N + 1 - m \ .$$

The first subscript indicates the row, the second the column in which the square (or cell) lies.

---

[40] See, for example, [A 12], pp. 111 ff.
[41] We think every high school graduate should know this method of proof.
[42] See [I 6].

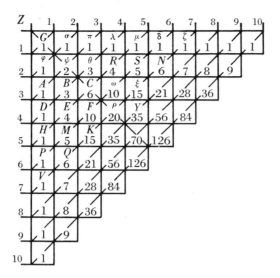

Fig. 14

Then the line containing the diagonal through squares q_{N1} and q_{1N} cuts from the whole schema* a system of squares arranged in the form of an isosceles right triangle. Each such array of squares leads to the formation of an "arithmetic" or "Pascal" triangle. The number N which determines the diagonal is called the order of the triangle.

In Pascal's day the double-subscript notation was not yet common, and hence he restricts himself (Figure 14) to denoting single squares by arbitrarily chosen Latin or Greek letters (G, ϕ, A, D, ...) . The Pascal triangle is then formed as follows: we imagine a number $a(m,n)$ written in each cell according to the following rule ([IV 2], p. 98):

> The number in the first cell by the right angle is arbitrary, but when this has been chosen, all the rest are determined. For that reason this number is called the 'generator' of the triangle. Every other number is then determined according to the following rule: the number in each cell is equal to that in the preceding cell of the vertical column, increased by that in the preceding cell of the horizontal row. Thus cell F, that is, the number in cell F, is equal to cell C increased by cell E, and similarly for the rest.

Today we can express the rule for constructing Pascal's triangle (with generator 1, as in Pascal's drawing, Figure 14) conveniently by means of a difference equation. In cell q_{mn} we write the number $a(m,n)$ satisfying the difference equation

(1) $$a(m,n) = a(m-1,n) + a(m,n-1)$$

* Translator's note: Here the schema is thought of as consisting of infinitely many rows, each containing infinitely many squares.

and the "initial conditions"

(1′) $a(0,n) = a(m,0) = 0$.

Starting with $a(1,1)$ (equal to 1 in Figure 14) and using (1) and (1′) we can easily calculate the numbers in the triangle, one after the other. From the law of formation, the symmetry

(2) $a(m,n) = a(n,m)$

of the arithmetic triangle is immediately clear. Pascal did not explicitly refer to the initial conditions (1′). He undoubtedly felt they could be taken for granted, since to the left of the first column and above the first line stands "nothing."

Pascal proves the following theorems on arithmetic triangles:

Theorem 1. In every A. T. (arithmetic triangle) the cells in the first row and those in the first column are equal to the generating number.

This follows at once from (1) and (1′).

Theorem 2. In every A. T., each cell is equal to the sum of the cells in the preceding row, from the one in the same column to the first.

We can state this theorem by means of the following formula:

(3) $a(m,n) = \sum_{i=1}^{n} a(m-1,i)$.

Pascal proves it in the following way. Let ω be any cell. Then[43] $\omega = R + C$, $C = \oplus + B$, $B = \psi + A$, and $A = \phi$. From these it follows at once that

$$\omega = R + \oplus + \psi + \phi .$$

Actually this does not prove the theorem for an arbitrary cell but only for $\omega = q_{3,4}$ (Figure 14). However, it is, of course, not hard to generalize this proof, using (1) and (1′) and following Pascal's proof for a specific example. In the notation of the day, "general" proofs could only be given by means of representative cases. In any case, Pascal knew that the proof he had given for ω could also be used for any other cell.

The next theorem can be proved in a similar way:

---

[43] See Figure 14.

Theorem 3.   In every A. T., each cell is equal to the sum of the cells in the preceding column, from the one in the same row to the first.

We shall not mention the many other laws Pascal read off from his triangle. Instead, we shall proceed to the place where he first uses induction. This happens where he uses the A. T. to solve combinatorial problems ([IV 2], p. 110).

In modern mathematics, the number of ways[44] of picking k elements from n is denoted by $\binom{n}{k}$. This number is easy to compute. It is known that

$$(4) \qquad \binom{n}{k} = \frac{n(n-1) \ldots (n-k+1)}{k!} = \frac{n!}{k!\,(n-k)!}.$$

This can be proved by mathematical induction, for example. Pascal knew neither our notation nor formula (4). He begins his remarks on combinatorial problems with simple, easily proved lemmas about[45] $\binom{n}{n}$, $\binom{n}{1}$, etc. Of importance for what follows is[46]

Theorem 4.   If there are four arbitrary numbers, of which the first is arbitrary, the second one greater than the first, the third arbitrary but not smaller than the second, and the fourth one greater than the third, then the number of combinations of the first in the third, increased by the number of combinations of the second in the third, is equal to the number of combinations of the second in the fourth.

In our modern notation this theorem can be expressed by the simple formula

$$(5) \qquad \binom{n}{k} + \binom{n}{k+1} = \binom{n+1}{k+1}, \; n > k \,.$$

We shall give a generalization of the proof given in the *Traité* for the case $n = 4, k = 2$.

Following Pascal, let us think of the objects to be chosen as different letters, of which the first is A. Then $\binom{n+1}{k+1}$ is the number of ways of choosing $k + 1$ out of $n + 1$ given letters ($n >$ k). Now the combinations of $k + 1$ letters can be divided into two classes: all the combinations which contain the letter A belong to the first, all the rest to the second. But the first class

---

[44] Pascal speaks of "k in n" combinations.
[45] We shall stick to modern terminology.
[46] Pascal's "Lemma IV."

contains exactly $\binom{n}{k}$ combinations. (To see this, we need only omit the ever-present A from the letters open to choice and from the letters chosen.) Further, we get all the combinations of the second class if from n letters (namely those from which we may choose, except for the A) we choose $k+1$ arbitrarily. From this argument, formula (5) follows at once.

We are now in a position to understand Pascal's inductive proof of his "Proposition I." We call the result to be proved

Theorem 5. In every A. T., the sum of the cells in any row is equal to the number of combinations of the row number in the order of the triangle.

Before we begin the proof, let us express this theorem in modern terminology. The order N of an arithmetic triangle is determined by the diagonal which passes through squares q_{1N} and q_{N1}. This diagonal cuts across precisely those squares q_{mn} for whose indices the equation

$$m + n - 1 = N$$

holds. These cells form the "base" of the triangle of order N. In the mth row of this triangle there are $N + 1 - m$ cells. Thus in our terminology Theorem 5 is as follows:

(6)
$$\sum_{i=1}^{N-m+1} a(m,i) = \binom{N}{m}.$$

Pascal says of the proof he is about to give that he will be brief, "although there are infinitely many cases." This remark makes it clear that he understood the importance of the new method of proof. As before, he gives his proof "in examples" (with his notation, nothing else is possible), but the principle of "mathematical induction" is used, and it guarantees the generality of the proof.

1. Clearly the equality holds for the first triangle, since the sum of the cells in its only row, namely G, is equal to the number of combinations of 1 (the number of the row) in 1 (the order of the triangle).

2. If there is an A. T. for which this assertion is correct, no matter what row one chooses (that is, in which the sum of the cells is equal to

the number of combinations of the row number in the order of the triangle), then (I claim) the following triangle has the same property. From this it follows that all A. T.'s satisfy this equation. For by the first lemma[47] the equation holds for the first triangle, and it is also obvious for the second. Then by the second lemma, the next triangle also has the same property, and the next, and so on forever.

Thus Pascal only needs to prove the statement numbered 2. It is true that once more he does this for a special case: assuming his theorem true for the third triangle, he proves its truth for the fourth.

Our modern, more suitable notation allows us to give this argument without restricting ourselves to a special case. Formula (6) is, as we have already observed, correct for $N = 1$. We now show that if it is correct for $N = k$, it is correct for $N = k + 1$. Thus by our "induction hypothesis," for every row of the triangle of order k,

$$(6') \qquad \sum_{i=1}^{k-m+1} a(m,i) = \binom{k}{m}$$

and we must prove that

$$(6'') \qquad \sum_{i=1}^{k-m+2} a(m,i) = \binom{k+1}{m}.$$

Now by (6') and (3),

$$(7) \qquad \sum_{i=1}^{k-m+2} a(m,i) = \sum_{i=1}^{k-m+1} a(m,i) + a(m,k-m+2)$$

$$= \binom{k}{m} + \sum_{i=1}^{k-m+2} a(m-1,i).$$

---

[47] This is the statement numbered 1 above.

By the induction assumption, however, for row $m - 1$ of the triangle of order k,

$$(6''') \qquad \sum_{i=1}^{k-m+2} a(m-1,i) = \binom{k}{m-1}.$$

Then from (7), (6''') and (5) we get

$$\sum_{i=1}^{k-m+2} a(m,i) = \binom{k}{m} + \binom{k}{m-1} = \binom{k+1}{m}, \text{ q.e.d.}$$

Even though Pascal only carries out this last argument for "an example," his method of mathematical induction provides the basis for many modern proofs.

Nowadays it is usual to draw Pascal's triangle not as he did but with the diagonals horizontal:

$$
\begin{array}{ccccccccc}
 & & & & 1 & & & & \\
 & & & 1 & & 1 & & & \\
 & & 1 & & 2 & & 1 & & \\
 & 1 & & 3 & & 3 & & 1 & \\
1 & & 4 & & 6 & & 4 & & 1 \\
\end{array}
$$

(8) $\quad 1 \qquad 5 \qquad 10 \qquad 10 \qquad 5 \qquad 1$

$\cdot \ \cdot$

We shall denote the numbers in *this* Pascal triangle by $B(N,m)$. Here the first subscript indicates the row in the new triangle (8) (that is, the diagonal in Figure 14), the second the position of the number in *this* row. If, in both cases, we start our numbering with zero, we have Theorem 5a. The number $B(N,m)$ in the mth place of the Nth row of triangle (8) is equal to the number of combinations of m elements N at a time:

$$(9) \qquad B(N,m) = \binom{N}{m}.$$

For by (6), (3) and (2),

$$(10) \qquad \binom{N}{m} = \sum_{i=1}^{N-m+1} a(m,i) = a(m+1, N-m+1)$$
$$= a(N-m+1, m+1) \,.$$

We now set

$$(11) \qquad a(N-m+1, m+1) = b(N+1, m+1)$$

and thereby identify each number in the triangle by its position in the diagonal. Thus, for example,

$$10 = \binom{5}{3} = a(4,3) = a(3,4) = b(6,4) \,.$$

Finally we start numbering with 0 by making the substitution

$$(12) \qquad b\,(N+1, m-1) = B\,(N,m) \,,$$

and thus (9) is proved from (10), (11) and (12).

On geometric proof

Pascal enriched various mathematical disciplines with important results, but he also had ideas on the nature and value of the "mathematical method." By his investigations of proof in geometry and of "the difference between the spirit of geometry and the spirit of intuition" he built a bridge between the mathematical thought of the ancients and our modern conception of the nature of the exact sciences.

In his *Methods and Psychology of the Scholar*[48] he gives a series of rules for definitions, axioms and proofs in geometry.

Rules for definitions
1. Define nothing which is itself so well known that there are no still clearer notions to use in defining it.
2. Leave undefined no unclear or ambiguous concepts.
3. In defining concepts, use only words which are well known or which have already been defined.

---

[48] [IV 1], p. 11 ff. The "rules" are on pages 42-43.

Rules for axioms

1. Of each necessary principle, no matter how clear and obvious it may be, ask first whether it is accepted.

2. Use as axioms only things which are completely self-evident.

Rules for proofs

1. Prove nothing that is so obvious that there is nothing clearer to use in proving it.

2. Prove every theorem which is not quite clear, and in its proof use only self-evident axioms or theorems which have already been accepted or proved.

3. In your mind, always put the definitions in place of the things defined, so as not to be deceived by the ambiguity of the concepts on which one has set limits by means of the definitions.

The improvement over Euclid's *Elements* lies in the recognition that not everything should or can be defined. All mathematical concepts and all proofs rest on certain things "which themselves are so well known there are no clearer concepts in terms of which to explain them." Euclid defines "point" and "line." Pascal, however, knows that there is a limit to what can be defined.

Of course, this does not mean Pascal was a formalist[49] in the modern sense. When he requires that only "self-evident things be used as axioms," we may infer that to him mathematical axioms were not simply a basis for a formal game — arbitrary postulates of which one requires only consistency and independence. For him they were clearly statements about something real. It was not until the nineteenth century that doubt was cast on the Platonic conception of the nature of mathematics.

In the last section of the work quoted, Pascal speaks of the "difference between the spirit of geometry and the spirit of intuition." It seems proper that we moderns, too, should reflect on the power and the limitations of the mathematical method. We quote without comment a few of Pascal's sentences on the subject from this section.

------

[49] See, for example, [A 12], Chapter X.

The principles (of the spirit of geometry) are evident, but removed from common use; and so it is an effort to turn one's head in that direction, since the habit is lacking . . . . .

But the principles of the spirit of intuition are in common use and in plain sight of everyone. One does not need to turn his head or force himself. One need only have good eyes. But they must be good, for the principles are so delicate and so numerous, it is almost impossible to see them all . . . .

And so it is seldom the case that mathematicians are men of intuition or men of intuition mathematicians, because the mathematicians want to treat these delicate things mathematically and thus make themselves laughable by beginning with definitions and going on to principles, which is not the right method for this way of forming judgments . . . .

If, on the other hand, one presents to intuitive people used to making up their minds at the first glance, propositions of which they understand nothing, and which one can only understand by means of dry definitions and principles, propositions they are not used to looking at in detail, they are so stupefied they let themselves be frightened off and lose all their eagerness . . . .

Thus the mathematicians who are merely mathematicians reason correctly, but only if one explains everything to them in terms of definitions and principles. Otherwise they are limited and insufferable, for they only reason correctly when they are dealing with very clear principles . . . .

And the intuitive people who are merely intuitive do not have the patience to descend to the first principles of speculative things, things which they have never seen in the world and which are not used at all.

Gottfried Wilhelm Leibniz

Datis ordinatis etiam quaesita sunt ordinata.
Leibniz ([V 3], p. 84)

Gottfried Wilhelm Leibniz

The polyhistor

In the twentieth century, science is a field for specialists. A man who wants to do original research must prepare himself by hard work in some narrow, special area of his science. He must first try to understand what others before him have devised or discovered. This material is so extensive that every investigator must become a specialist. He must know a great deal, but what he knows does not cover a wide field. It is concentrated in the fields of science which are important for the problem he has chosen. In our academic education there is a vital question of how to overcome this isolation of research workers without jeopardizing the concentration of their efforts.

Thus it is with a certain regret that one looks back on a period in which a highly gifted and hard-working scholar could master all that was known at the time. It is said that Gottfried Wilhelm Leibniz (1646-1716) was the last to achieve this state of universal knowledge. He earned a master's degree in philosophy and a bachelor's degree in law[50] at Leipzig; he talked with alchemists and physicists like Otto von Guericke and tried his hand at papers on problems in mechanics. His trip to Paris in 1672 led him to take up the study of mathematics. He met Huygens, who called his attention to Pascal's mathematical writings. Add to this the fact that the philosopher of the "preestablished harmony" entered the field of theology with his *Théodicée* and it becomes clear that Leibniz had, in truth, a universal mind, and did stimulating work in many areas of intellectual life. We cannot undertake here the task of assessing the whole breadth of his activity.

In the field of mathematics, Leibniz was entirely self-taught. He attended no lectures on mathematics but was stimulated by the Paris circle to read mathematical publications and to do work of his own. Because his early training was of this sort, it is easily understandable that he sometimes discovered theorems that others had found before him. It is also true that in his day communication between scholars through publication in widely circulated scientific journals was not common. Thus it could easily happen that important discoveries for which the time was ripe were made independently by different scholars. The founding of the infinitesimal calculus by Newton and Leibniz is one example of such a duplication, the discovery of non-Euclidean geometry by Bolyai and Lobachevski in the nineteenth century another.

---

[50] Later, at Altdorf, he was awarded the degree of *Doctor juris utriusque*.

Today it no longer seems so important to us which investigator can claim priority of publication. It is not the date of a publication that counts but the contents. Every scholar has his own way of attacking problems, and so it can perfectly well happen that the second work to appear is no less important than the first. Newton looked at the problems of infinitesimal calculus from the point of view of physics. Leibniz started from the tangent problem and created a practical calculus which is still in use today. After many years of controversy over the question of priority, it can now be considered as established that Newton's work was done a few years earlier than that of the German scholar. On the other hand, it also seems certain that Leibniz made his discoveries independently of Newton and his fellow countrymen.[51]

In discussions of Leibniz's mathematical achievements it is usual to speak of his founding the infinitesimal calculus. It should not be forgotten, however, that he also did stimulating work in many other fields of mathematics. Until the ninteenth and twentieth centuries, his proposal of a "universal language of ideas" understandable to people of all lands was not properly appreciated. In 1666, at the age of twenty, he earned the right to teach at the University of Leipzig with his paper on this subject entitled *Dissertatio de Arte Combinatoria*. Nevertheless, his idea of a "language of concepts" was not taken up at that time. It was not until the work of George Boole[52] (who probably did not know Leibniz's paper) that an algebra came into existence which can be called a realization of Leibniz's ideas.

In addition, Leibniz made important contributions to the theory of determinants and the calculus of finite differences.[53] If we want, in the short compass of a chapter, to document his work as a mathematician with examples, we are in something of a dilemma. What shall we choose? We must and can[54] dispense with a connected account of the origins of his infinitesimal calculus. However, his own philosophy justifies our illustrating the whole with a typical example — just as every "Monad" is a "living mirror of the universe," so the working methods of an investigator can be seen in a few suitably chosen examples.

---

[51] See, for example, [V 4], [V 7], [V 8] and [V 9].
[52] See Chapter VII.
[53] For more on this topic see, for example, [A 4], p. 125 ff., and [V 5].
[54] A detailed account is given in [V 7].

Gottfried Wilhelm Leibniz

The "harmonic triangle"

When Leibniz was being introduced to the problems of mathematics by Huygens in Paris, his teacher assigned him the problem of summing the infinite series

$$
\text{(1)} \qquad \frac{2}{1 \cdot 2} + \frac{2}{2 \cdot 3} + \frac{2}{3 \cdot 4} + \frac{2}{4 \cdot 5} + \cdots .
$$

The terms of this series (1) are the reciprocals of the Triangular Numbers[55]

$$
d_n = \binom{n + 1}{2} = \frac{n(n + 1)}{2} .
$$

Leibniz showed he was equal to the problem. He wrote the terms of the series (1) in the form

$$
\frac{2}{2 \cdot 3} = 2(\tfrac{1}{2} - \tfrac{1}{3}) , \quad \frac{2}{3 \cdot 4} = 2(\tfrac{1}{3} - \tfrac{1}{4}) , \ldots , \quad \delta_n = \frac{1}{d_n} = 2\left(\frac{1}{n} - \frac{1}{n + 1} \right) .
$$

Then one gets as an "approximating sum" S_n for (1),

$$
\text{(2)} \qquad S_n = \frac{2}{1 \cdot 2} + \frac{2}{2 \cdot 3} + \cdots + \frac{2}{n(n + 1)} = 2\left(1 - \frac{1}{n + 1} \right)
$$

and finally (in modern notation)

$$
S = \lim S_n = 2 .
$$

It is typical of the turn of our investigator's mind toward the universal that he later generalized this procedure and was then able to read off from his "harmonic triangle" many convergent series.[56] The harmonic triangle is a counterpart of Pascal's arithmetic triangle in the form of Eq. (8) Chap. IV:

---

[55] Cf. p. 3.
[56] See [V 5]. This paper also contains a detailed list of sources, references to Leibniz's manuscripts, etc.

(3)

$$
\begin{array}{ccccccccccccc}
 & & & & & & \dfrac{1}{1} & & & & & & \\[2mm]
 & & & & & \dfrac{1}{2} & & \dfrac{1}{2} & & & & & \\[2mm]
 & & & & \dfrac{1}{3} & & \dfrac{1}{6} & & \dfrac{1}{3} & & & & \\[2mm]
 & & & \dfrac{1}{4} & & \dfrac{1}{12} & & \dfrac{1}{12} & & \dfrac{1}{4} & & & \\[2mm]
 & & \dfrac{1}{5} & & \dfrac{1}{20} & & \dfrac{1}{30} & & \dfrac{1}{20} & & \dfrac{1}{5} & & \\[2mm]
 & \dfrac{1}{6} & & \dfrac{1}{30} & & \dfrac{1}{60} & & \dfrac{1}{60} & & \dfrac{1}{30} & & \dfrac{1}{6} & \\[2mm]
\dfrac{1}{7} & & \dfrac{1}{42} & & \dfrac{1}{105} & & \dfrac{1}{140} & & \dfrac{1}{105} & & \dfrac{1}{42} & & \dfrac{1}{7}
\end{array}
$$

. . . .

This triangle of numbers is characterized by the following properties:

(I)   The nth row[57] begins and ends with $1/(n+1)$.

(II) Every number is the sum of the two below it.

The corresponding statements about Pascal's triangle (in the form of Eq. (8) Chap. IV) are

(I′) Every row begins and ends with 1.

(II′) Every number not on the boundry is the sum of the two above it.

It will be convenient to use the language of modern mathematics in establishing the properties of the harmonic triangle (3). Following Hofmann and Wieleitner we shall denote the general number in (3) by $\begin{bmatrix} n \\ k \end{bmatrix}$, where n indicates the row, k the place in the row. Then Rule (II) can be stated as follows:

(4)
$$
\begin{bmatrix} n \\ k \end{bmatrix} = \begin{bmatrix} n+1 \\ k \end{bmatrix} + \begin{bmatrix} n+1 \\ k+1 \end{bmatrix} .
$$

---

[57] We begin numbering with zero.

Further, by Rule (I)

(5)
$$\begin{bmatrix} n \\ 0 \end{bmatrix} = \frac{1}{n+1}, \qquad n = 0, 1, 2, \ldots .$$

Equations (4) and (5) are the counterparts to the well-known formulas

(4')
$$\binom{n}{k} = \binom{n-1}{k-1} + \binom{n-1}{k}$$

and

(5')
$$\binom{n}{0} = 1$$

for the numbers in Pascal's triangle.[58] The numbers in (3) can be computed by first writing down the "oblique row" corresponding to $k = 0$

$$\sigma_0 : 1, \tfrac{1}{2}, \tfrac{1}{3}, \tfrac{1}{4}, \ldots$$

then using (4) to determine, one after the other, the numbers in the oblique row σ_1, etc. That every row ends with $1/(n+1)$ must be proved. This fact and, more generally, the symmetry of the harmonic triangle, follow from the formula

(6)
$$\begin{bmatrix} n \\ k \end{bmatrix} = \frac{1}{(n+1)\binom{n}{k}} = \frac{k!(n-k)!}{(n+1)!}$$

which establishes a relation between the numbers in the harmonic triangle and those in Pascal's triangle. Equation (6) can be proved easily by mathematical induction. Clearly it gives the right results for the first oblique row, since by (6)

$$\begin{bmatrix} n \\ 0 \end{bmatrix} = \frac{0!\,n!}{(n+1)!} = \frac{1}{n+1}.$$

Now assume that (6) holds for the mth oblique row, that is, for $k = m - 1$.

---

[58] Cf. Chapter IV Eq. (5).

From (4) and the induction hypothesis it follows that

$$\begin{bmatrix} n \\ m \end{bmatrix} = \begin{bmatrix} n-1 \\ m-1 \end{bmatrix} - \begin{bmatrix} n \\ m-1 \end{bmatrix}$$

$$= \frac{(m-1)!\,(n-m)!}{n!} - \frac{(m-1)!\,(n-m+1)!}{(n+1)!}$$

$$= \frac{m!\,(n-m)!}{(n+1)!}\,.$$

From (6) one can immediately infer the symmetry of the harmonic triangle:

(7)
$$\begin{bmatrix} n \\ k \end{bmatrix} = \begin{bmatrix} n \\ n-k \end{bmatrix}$$

and, further, the important limit

(8)
$$\lim_{n \to \infty} \begin{bmatrix} n \\ k \end{bmatrix} = 0\,.$$

Equation (8) can be used to find the sum of the numbers in an oblique row. For the partial sums

$$S_k(N) = \sum_{n=k}^{N} \begin{bmatrix} n \\ k \end{bmatrix},\ k = 1, 2, 3, \dots,$$

equation (4) shows that

(9)
$$S_k(N) = \sum_{n=k}^{N} \left(\begin{bmatrix} n-1 \\ k-1 \end{bmatrix} - \begin{bmatrix} n \\ k-1 \end{bmatrix} \right) = \begin{bmatrix} k-1 \\ k-1 \end{bmatrix} - \begin{bmatrix} N \\ k-1 \end{bmatrix}$$

and from this and (8) it follows that

(10)
$$\lim_{n \to \infty} S_k(N) = S_k = \sum_{n=k}^{\infty} \begin{bmatrix} n \\ k \end{bmatrix} = \begin{bmatrix} k-1 \\ k-1 \end{bmatrix} = \frac{1}{k}\,.$$

From this we can get, for example, the series

$$2 \cdot S_1 = 2 \begin{bmatrix} 0 \\ 0 \end{bmatrix} = \frac{2}{1} = 1 + \frac{1}{3} + \frac{1}{6} + \frac{1}{10} + \cdots$$

(11)
$$3 \cdot S_2 = 3 \begin{bmatrix} 1 \\ 1 \end{bmatrix} = \frac{3}{2} = 1 + \frac{1}{4} + \frac{1}{10} + \frac{1}{20} + \cdots$$

$$4 \cdot S_3 = 4 \begin{bmatrix} 2 \\ 2 \end{bmatrix} = \frac{4}{3} = 1 + \frac{1}{5} + \frac{1}{15} + \frac{1}{35} + \cdots .$$

These series are also in Leibniz's manuscript. He obtained them by using the rules of formation (I) and (II), though not, of course, in the form given here.

However, in addition to (11), Leibniz gives the series

(12)
$$\frac{1}{0} = 1 + \frac{1}{2} + \frac{1}{3} + \cdots .$$

This series is obtained by a formal argument from analogy: one need only add the series for $k = 0$ to the collection of series for $(k + 1)S_k$ given in (11). Equation (12) may be interpreted as saying that the series obtained in this way diverges.

This is true, but the argument from analogy is nevertheless not valid. For (4) holds only for $k \geq 0$, so (9) holds only for $k \geq 1$. Thus we have an example both of the power and of the limitations of Leibniz's way of working. Perhaps it was his belief in the harmony of all that is knowable[59] that made him prone to such daring arguments from analogy. Modern mathematicians are aware that only under specific hypotheses can one reason from the "order of the given" to the "order of the sought."

Leibniz's series

Today Leibniz's series

(13)
$$\pi/4 = 1 - \frac{1}{3} + \frac{1}{5} - \frac{1}{7} + \cdots$$

is usually derived from the series for arc tan x. However, Leibniz happened on this representation by way of a unique treatment of the problem of finding the area of a circle. In our account of his method we shall not hesitate to speak of "infinitesimal triangles" and "neighboring points," as was usual in

---

[59] See the motto at the beginning of this chapter.

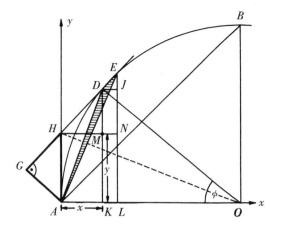

Fig. 15

his day. The reader who is accustomed to the precise language of modern analysis should at this point quiet his mathematical conscience with a fairly powerful sleeping pill, and then later try to translate this argument into the language of modern calculus.

Leibniz wishes to determine the area of a quarter of a circle (of radius 1). To do this he divides the quarter circle into an isosceles right triangle (ABO in Figure 15) and a segment (with arc AB).[60]

The quadrature of the segment is then accomplished by dividing it into "infinitesimal" triangles ADE, using "neighboring" points D and E on the circumference. Let K and L be the feet of the perpendiculars from D and E to the x-axis, AO. Let H be the intersection of the line DE and the tangent at A (the y-axis), G the foot of the perpendicular from A to the line DE. Finally, the perpendicular from D to EL gives us the typical infinitesimal triangle DEJ.

It is clear at once that triangles DEJ and AHG are similar, from which follows

$$DE : DJ = AH : AG$$

or

$$AG \cdot DE = AH \cdot DJ .$$

Now suppose the parallel to the x-axis through H meets the segments DK and JL in M and N. Then if $F(ADE)$ is the area of the infinitesimal triangle ADE,

$$F(ADE) = \tfrac{1}{2}AG \cdot ds = \tfrac{1}{2}F(KLMN)$$

or

(14) $$\tfrac{1}{2}AG \cdot ds = \tfrac{1}{2}y\,dx .$$

---

[60] We follow here largely [V 4]. This paper contains detailed information on the manuscripts.

Gottfried Wilhelm Leibniz

Here ds stands for DE, y for $AH = KM$, x for AK and dx for $DJ = MN = KL$.

Further, we let ϕ be the angle DOA and thus obtain

$$(15) \qquad\qquad x = AK = 1 - \cos\phi = 2\sin^2\phi/2 \, .$$

Now AH is tangent to the circle, and we can also say that the secant DE joining neighboring points "touches" the circle. Hence

$$(16) \qquad\qquad y = AH = KM = \tan\phi/2 \, .$$

Since

$$\sin^2\alpha = \frac{\tan^2\alpha}{1 + \tan^2\alpha}$$

it follows from (15) and (16) that

$$(17) \qquad\qquad x(1 + y^2) = 2y^2 \, .$$

This cubic equation determines the curve on which lie all possible points M with coordinates x and y. Using (14) we now replace the summation of all the triangles ADE by an integration of y with respect to x:

$$(18) \qquad\qquad S = \tfrac{1}{2} \int AG \, ds = \tfrac{1}{2} \int y \, dx \, .$$

Here S is the required area of the segment. Now for every curve $y = y(x)$ the integration with respect to x can be replaced by an integration with respect to y. Thus, in our case from (18) we get

$$(19) \qquad S = \tfrac{1}{2} \int y \, dx = \tfrac{1}{2} x y - \tfrac{1}{2} \int x \, dy = \tfrac{1}{2} x y - \int \frac{y^2}{1 + y^2} dy \, .$$

Then Leibniz develops the fraction in (19) in a series:

$$(20) \qquad\qquad \frac{y^2}{1 + y^2} = y^2 - y^4 + y^6 - \dots \, .$$

Integrating term by term[61] gives

$$(21) \qquad\qquad S = \tfrac{1}{2} xy - y^3/3 + y^5/5 - \dots \, .$$

---

[61] From the modern point of view, this procedure requires a proof of the uniform convergence of the series (20).

If $\phi = \pi/2$ and $x = y = 1$, (21) implies that

$$S = \tfrac{1}{2} - \tfrac{1}{3} + \tfrac{1}{5} - \tfrac{1}{7} + \tfrac{1}{9} - \ldots .$$

If, finally, we add the area of the right triangle ABO to this, we get for the area of a quarter of the unit circle:

$$F = \pi/4 = 1 - \tfrac{1}{3} + \tfrac{1}{5} - \tfrac{1}{7} + \tfrac{1}{9} - \ldots .$$

The "infinitely small"

Through the work of Cauchy, Weierstrass, and other ninteenth century mathematicians, analysis has been given a foundation which avoids the dubious notion of the infinitely small.[62] It is not hard to translate Leibniz's derivation of the series for $\pi/4$ into modern terms.

However, in order to understand Leibniz's way of thinking and that of his contemporaries, one must know what they meant by the infinitely small and the "principle of continuity." For that reason we shall quote, without comment, several passages from the correspondence between Varignon and Leibniz, which concerns this topic ([V 3], pp. 94-100).

Varignon to Leibniz

Paris, November 28, 1701

Permit me to assure you of my deepest respect and at the same time to inform you of a work which is being circulated here under your name. It concerns the disagreement between Mr. Rolle and myself, of which you know, regarding your infinitesimal calculus, which he terms false and to which he attributes errors in reasoning. The Abbé Galloys, who is really behind the whole thing, is spreading the report here that you have explained that you mean by the "differential" or the "infinitely small" a very small, but nevertheless constant and definite quantity, such as the earth in relation to the heavens or a grain of sand in relation to the earth. I, on the other hand, have called a thing infinitely small or the differential of a quantity if that quantity is inexhaustible in comparison with the thing. Thus I have called infinite or indefinite everything which is inexhaustible, while

---

[62] See Chapter VIII.

Gottfried Wilhelm Leibniz

I have called infinitely or indefinitely small everything with respect to which a given quantity is inexhaustible. From this I have drawn the conclusion that in the differential calculus the terms infinite, indefinite, inexhaustible in size, greater than any assignable quantity, indeterminately large; like the terms infinitely or indefinitely small, smaller than any assignable quantity, indeterminately small; are entirely synonymous. I entreat you to give me your verdict on this matter, so that I can tell the opponents of this calculus to stop misusing your name in order to deceive ignorant people and fools . . . .

Leibniz to Varignon

Hanover, February 2, 1702

I no longer remember the exact terms I used; my intention, however, was to show that one does not need to make mathematical analysis depend on metaphysical quarrels; in other words, that one need not assert that there exist in nature lines which in comparison with our ordinary one are, in the strict sense, infinitely small . . . .

In order, therefore, to avoid these subtle matters of dispute and because I wanted my ideas to be generally understood, I contented myself with explaining the infinite as the incomparable. In other words, I assumed there were quantities which were incomparably larger or smaller than ours. For in this way one obtains arbitrarily many degrees of incomparable quantities, in so far as an incomparably much smaller quantity may be disregarded when one is calculating an incomparably much larger one. Thus a tiny particle of the magnetic material which can pass through glass is not comparable with a grain of sand, or a grain of sand with the earth, or, finally, the earth with the heavens.

One must remember, however, that incomparably small quantities, even when understood in the popular sense, are by no means constant and determined. On the contrary, since they may be made as small as we like, they play the same part in geometric reasoning as the infinitely small in the strict sense. For if an antagonist denies the correctness of our theorems, our calculations show that the error is smaller than any given quantity, since it is in our power to decrease the incomparably small, which one can always assume as small as he likes, as much as is necessary for our purpose. This is perhaps what you mean by the inexhaustible, and there is no doubt that therein lies the rigorous proof of our infinitesimal calculus.

One must not think, however, that the science of the infinite is depreciated and traced back to fictions by this explanation. For there always remains, if I may express myself as the Scholastics do, a syncategorematical infinity. For example, it is always true that 2 is equal to

$$1 + \tfrac{1}{2} + \tfrac{1}{4} + \cdots,$$

that is, equal to an infinite series containing all fractions whose numerators are 1 and whose denominators form a geometric progression . . . .

Carl Friedrich Gauss

Pauca sed matura.[63]

Gauss

[63] *Pauca sed matura* is the inscription on the seal of Gauss. The three words are arranged around a laurel tree that has only a few berries, but those are ripe.

"Prince of mathematicians"

When Carl Friedrich Gauss died, on Feburary 23, 1855, the King of Hanover had a memorial coin struck off with the dedication, "Georgius V Rex Hannoverae Mathematicorum Principi." It is not hard to explain why, to his contemporaries, Gauss was the "prince of mathematicians." One can point out the sweep of what he accomplished, ranging from pure number theory, algebra and analysis, to applied mathematics, astronomy and physics. However, such an enumeration is convincing only if in addition one can give detailed appreciations of individual accomplishments.

We do not have space for that here.[64] However, in Gauss' case one can justify the royal dedication in another way. His publications are mature; the elegance and compactness of his presentation make it clear to the initiated that each of his papers is the work of a master. This characteristic of his works impresses the modern reader again and again. It stems from a maturity as a human being that we today do not always possess: Gauss could wait. He could wait until he found the definitive form for a proof. He once wrote to his friend Schumacher about this:

> You know that I write slowly. This is chiefly because I am never satisfied until I have said as much as possible in a few words, and writing briefly takes far more time than writing at length.

And Sartorius von Walterhausen says in his obituary for Gauss:[65]

> Gauss always strove to give his investigations the form of finished works of art. He did not rest until he had succeeded, and hence he never published a work until it had achieved the form he wanted. He used to say that when a fine building was finished, the scaffolding should no longer be visible.

For this reason, the works of the prince of mathematicians have a cold beauty; it is disturbing to those of his readers who would like to find out how he discovered his proofs. Abel says of him: "He is like the fox, who effaces his

---

[64] A detailed appreciation of Gauss' accomplishments is given in [VII 3]. The biography by Worbs [VI 2] gives a good picture of his personality.

[65] We quote from [VI 2], p. 130.

tracks in the sand with his tail," and Jacobi calls his proofs "stark and frozen, . . . so that one must first thaw them out."[66]

Working according to the principle "pauca sed matura" had consequences for Gauss which a less fertile mind would have found very annoying. Because he waited so long before publishing his ideas, it sometimes happened that others anticipated him. That is what happened with the theory of elliptic functions. Jacobi and Abel are credited with being the founders of this theory, but we now know from Gauss' notebooks that by 1800 he had already developed the main features of the theory. It was much the same with non-Euclidean geometry. He kept his ideas to himself (because he feared "the outcry of the Boeotians," as he wrote in 1829 in a letter to Bessel), and Lobachevski and Bolyai became the founders of this important new discipline in mathematics.

We close this section with an illustration of Gauss' ability "to compress every mathematical discussion into its most elegant and simplest form" ([VI 2], p. 227).

In a letter of August 22, 1836, to Gauss, Schumacher presents a construction, due to Rümcker, of the tangents to an ellipse through a point P outside the ellipse (Figure 16).

Rümcker draws any four secants PA_iB_i ($i = 1,2,3,4$) through P, and also the segments A_1B_2, A_2B_1, A_3B_4, A_4B_3 with intersections C and D. Then the line CD meets the ellipse[67] in the points Q_1 and Q_2 of tangency of the tangents t_1 and t_2 through P which we are looking for. Schumacher observes that this "pretty problem" can be solved even more simply: three secants will do, since the intersection of A_2B_3 and A_3B_2 also lies on the line CD.

Finally, in an answer written six days later, Gauss has an even simpler solution: he manages with only two secants, observing that the intersection R of the lines A_1A_2 and B_1B_2 also lies on the line CD.

As a good example of Gauss' way of working we give next one of his proofs of the Fundamental Theorem of Algebra. Gauss gave many proofs of the fact that every algebraic equation with real coefficients has at least one (real or complex) solution. His thesis, presented to Pfaff in Helmstedt in 1797, is the first proof of this important theorem. In the next section we give the purely analytic proof which appeared in 1816 in the "Göttinger Gelehrten Anzeigen."

---

[66] Compare this with the point of view of Weierstrass (in the motto of Chapter VIII, p. 85).
[67] CD is the polar of the point P.

Carl Friedrich Gauss

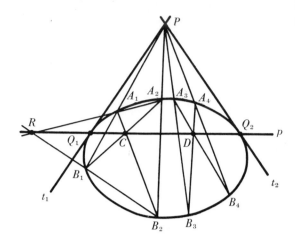

Fig. 16

And now we shall leave it to the reader to decide whether he will merely admire the elegance and clarity with which this proof is presented, or whether he will also look for the tracks which the fox "effaced with his tail," in other words, whether he wants to find out how Gauss discovered this solution. In the main we follow his presentation, but we add a few remarks to make it easier to check his deductions.

An analytic proof of the Fundamental Theorem of Algebra

We must show that every polynomial

$$(1) \qquad f(z) = z^m + A_1 z^{m-1} + A_2 z^{m-2} + \cdots + A_{m-1} z + A_m$$

with real coefficients $A\mu(\mu = 1,2, \ldots, m)$ has at least one (real or complex) zero. Let

$$z = x + iy = r(\cos \phi + i \sin \phi) \,,$$

$$(2)$$

$$f(z) = t + iu = t(r,\phi) + iu(r,\phi)$$

so that

$$|f(z)|^2 = t^2 + u^2 \,.$$

If $f(z)$ were everywhere different from zero, the function

$$\frac{g\,(r,\phi)}{(t^2 + u^2)^2}$$

would be continuous and differentiable everywhere in the finite plane as long as the function $g(r,\phi)$ in the numerator has these properties. (The denominator would have no zeros.) In that case one could evaluate the integral

$$(3) \qquad \Omega = \iint\limits_{K(R)} \frac{g\,(r,\phi)}{(t^2 + u^2)^2} \, dr \, d\phi$$

over a circle $K(R)$ with radius R and center the origin, using a well known theorem of real analysis, *either* by integrating first with respect to r from 0 to R and then with respect to ϕ from 0 to 2π, *or* by integrating in the opposite order. *The value of Ω is independent of the order of integration.* If we can show that for a certain function $g(r,\phi)$ the order of integration in the evaluation of the integral (3) *does* make a difference, it follows that the hypothesis $f(z) \neq 0$ is false. Thus the Fundamental Theorem of Algebra will be proved if we show the existence of such an integral (3).

To do this we introduce, following Gauss, the definitions

$$t' = mr^m \cos m\phi + (m-1) A_1 r^{m-1} \cos (m-1) \phi + \cdots$$
$$+ A_{m-1} r \cos \phi$$
$$u' = mr^m \sin m\phi + (m-1) A_1 r^{m-1} \sin (m-1) \phi + \cdots$$
$$+ A_{m-1} r \sin \phi$$

(4)

$$t'' = m^2 r^m \cos m\phi + (m-1)^2 A_1 r^{m-1} \cos (m-1) + \cdots$$
$$+ A_{m-1} r \cos \phi$$
$$u'' = m^2 r^m \sin m\phi + (m-1)^2 A_1 r^{m-1} \sin (m-1) \phi + \cdots$$
$$+ A_{m-1} r \sin \phi$$

The quantities defined in (4) are related to the real part

(5) $$t(r,\phi) = r^m \cos m\phi + A_1 r^{m-1} \cos (m-1) \phi + \cdots$$
$$+ A_{m-1} r \cos \phi + A_m$$

and the imaginary part

(5') $$u(r,\phi) = r^m \sin m\phi + A_1 r^{m-1} \sin (m-1) \phi + \cdots$$
$$+ A_{m-1} r \sin \phi$$

of the given function $f(x + iy)$ as follows:

(6) $$t' = u_\phi , \quad u' = -t_\phi , \quad t'' = -t_{\phi\phi} , \quad u'' = -u_{\phi\phi} .$$

We note further the relations

$$t_{\phi\phi} = -r \cdot u_{\phi r} , \quad u_{\phi\phi} = -r \cdot t_{\phi r}$$

(7)

$$u_\phi = r \cdot t_r , \quad t_\phi = -r \cdot u_r$$

Carl Friedrich Gauss

which are easily deduced from (4), (5), (5') and (6). Finally we introduce the following additional definitions:

$$T = R^m \cos\frac{\pi}{4} + A_1 R^{m-1} \cos\left(\frac{\pi}{4} + \phi\right) + \cdots + A_m \cos\left(\frac{\pi}{4} + m\phi\right)$$

(8)

$$U = R^m \sin\frac{\pi}{4} + A_1 R^{m-1} \sin\left(\frac{\pi}{4} + \phi\right) + \cdots + A_m \sin\left(\frac{\pi}{4} + m\phi\right)$$

and

$$T' = m R^m \cos\frac{\pi}{4} + A_1(m-1) R^{m-1} \cos\left(\frac{\pi}{4} + \phi\right) + \cdots + A_{m-1} R \cos$$

(8')
$$\left(\frac{\pi}{4} + (m-1)\phi\right)$$

$$U' = m R^m \sin\frac{\pi}{4} + A_1(m-1) R^{m-1} \sin\left(\frac{\pi}{4} + \phi\right) + \cdots + A_{m-1} R \sin$$

$$\left(\frac{\pi}{4} + (m-1)\phi\right).$$

Here R is an arbitrary positive, real number satisfying the inequality

(9)
$$R > \max\left(\sqrt[n]{m |A_n| \cdot \sqrt{2}}\right), n = 1, 2, \ldots, m.$$

For this choice of R the quantities T, U, T' and U' are always positive. This can be seen at once for T, for example, if we write it in the form

(10)
$$T = \sum_{n=1}^{m} \frac{R^{m-n}}{m \cdot \sqrt{2}}\left[R^n + m A_n \sqrt{2} \cos\left(\frac{\pi}{4} + n\phi\right)\right].$$

Since $| \cos(\pi/4 + n\phi) | \leq 1$, and (9) holds, none of the terms of (10) is negative. Since, further, it is clear that *not all* of them vanish, T is always positive. A similar argument can be used for U, T' and U'.

Finally, we observe that for $r = R$ the quantities t, u, t' and u' defined by (5), (5') and (4) have the following values:

$$t(R, \phi) = T \cos\left(\frac{\pi}{4} + m\phi\right) + U \sin\left(\frac{\pi}{4} + m\phi\right)$$

$$u(R, \phi) = T \sin\left(\frac{\pi}{4} + m\phi\right) - U \cos\left(\frac{\pi}{4} + m\phi\right)$$

(11)
$$t'(R, \phi) = T' \cos\left(\frac{\pi}{4} + m\phi\right) + U' \sin\left(\frac{\pi}{4} + m\phi\right)$$

$$u'(R, \phi) = T' \sin\left(\frac{\pi}{4} + m\phi\right) - U' \cos\left(\frac{\pi}{4} + m\phi\right).$$

From these it follows at once that if $r = R$, the quantities $t^2 + u^2 = T^2 + U^2$ and $tt' + uu' = TT' + UU'$ are both positive.

(12)
$$t^2 + u^2 = T^2 + U^2 > 0$$
$$tt' + uu'' = TT' + UU' > 0 .$$

After these preparatory steps we proceed to the evaluation of the integral

(2′)
$$\Omega = \int_{K(R)} y \, dr \, d\phi ,$$

where

(13)
$$y = \frac{(t^2 + u^2)(tt'' + uu'') + (tu' - ut')^2 - (tt' + uu')^2}{r \, (t^2 + u^2)^2}$$

Here $K(R)$ is a circle about the origin with radius R satisfying the inequality (9). Note that every term occurring in the numerator of (13) has a factor r, so the r in the denominator can be cancelled. We now assume that $t^2 + u^2$ does not vanish in the circle $K(R)$, and evaluate (2′) by integrating first with respect to ϕ, then with respect to r:

(2″)
$$\Omega = \int_{r=0}^{R} \left(\int_{\phi=0}^{2\pi} y \, d\phi \right) dr.$$

Now the inner integral in (2″) can be written in the form

(14)
$$\int y \, d\phi = \frac{tu' - ut'}{r \, (t^2 + u^2)} .$$

This is easily seen by differentiating the quotient

(15)
$$q \, (r,\phi) = \frac{tu' - ut'}{r \, (t^2 + u^2)}$$

with respect to ϕ. In carrying out this calculation (which, following Gauss' example we leave to the reader), it is convenient to use (6) and replace t' and u' in (15) by the partial derivatives u_ϕ and $- t_\phi$.

From (5) and (4) we see at once that $q\,(r,0) = q\,(r,2\pi) = 0$. Hence

(16)
$$\Omega = \int_{r=0}^{R}\left(\int_{\phi=0}^{2\pi} y\,d\phi\right)dr = 0.$$

However, one can also evaluate (2') by integrating first with respect to r. Then

(2''')
$$\Omega = \int_{\phi=0}^{2\pi}\left(\int_{r=0}^{R} y\,dr\right)d\phi.$$

This time the inner integral can be written in the form

(17)
$$\int_{0}^{R} y\,dr = \left[\frac{tt' + uu'}{t^2 + u^2}\right]_{0}^{R}.$$

Here too one can convince himself of the correctness of this assertion by finding the partial derivative of

(18)
$$q^*(r,\,\phi) = \frac{tt' + uu'}{t^2 + u^2}$$

with respect to r. To do this we use (6) to write q^* in the form

(18')
$$q^*(r,\,\phi) = \frac{tu_\phi - ut_\phi}{t^2 + u^2}$$

Using the quotient rule and taking account of (6), (7) and (13), a simple calculation gives

$$\frac{\partial q^*}{\partial r} = -\frac{(t^2 + u^2)\,(tt_{\phi\phi} + uu_{\phi\phi}) + (tu_\phi - ut_\phi)^2 - (tt_\phi + uu_\phi)^2}{r\,(t^2 + u^2)^2} = y$$

Thus (17) is proved.

Using (12), and noting that $t'\,(0,\phi) = u'\,(0,\phi) = 0$, it follows from (17) that

$$\int_{0}^{R} y\,dr = \frac{TT' + UU'}{T^2 + U^2} > 0.$$

Thus our integral Ω must also be positive:

(19)
$$\Omega = \int\limits_0^{2\pi} \frac{TT' + UU'}{T^2 + U^2}\, d\phi > 0 \,.$$

Since (19) and (16) are contradictory, the hypothesis that $f(z) \neq 0$ is false.

George Boole

*Pure mathematics was discovered by Boole in a
work called* "The Laws of Thought."

B. Russell[68]

[68] Quoted from [VII 2], the back flap of the dust jacket.

George Boole

The self-taught man

It seems that in our era of specialization an admirable type of mathematician is becoming extinct: the self-taught man who, without a complete knowledge of the technical literature, thinks his way into a problem and following his own path, penetrates into new territory, previously closed to the experts. There are still, of course, mathematical cranks who, untroubled by any knowledge of the field, try to solve problems which are demonstrably unsolvable. The editors of mathematical journals and the authors of popular books are acquainted with such correspondents, hard to deal with because of the consistent tenacity of their misunderstanding.

In earlier times, this unpleasant sort of self-taught man was not the only kind. In the field of number theory, for example, there were highly gifted outsiders who, as late as the 19th century, worked out results the experts were forced to recognize. As a result of increasing specialization the chances for such independent thinkers are now much smaller.

E. T. Bell, the British historian of mathematics, says ([A 7], p. 478) that his fellow countrymen are addicted to that stubborn sort of mathematical brooding which pays no attention to what others have already thought or written. They do mathematics because they enjoy working with numbers and figures, just as others like to play cricket.

In the field of technical mathematics, one such outsider was George Boole (1815-1864), who "discovered pure mathematics," according to no less a man than Bertrand Russell. His father, John Boole, was a cobbler in Lincoln, and in addition, a remarkable philosopher. He built optical instruments and invited people "to observe the works of God in a spirit of veneration" ([VII 5], p. 67). Years after Boole's death, when someone praised the author of *The Laws of Thought* to his mother, she replied: "Ah, but you didn't know his father? He really *was* a philosopher." And George Boole's wife once said of her father-in-law, "He seemed to be capable of doing everything but look after his own business."

Though the family of John Boole was comfortably off, George did not get his education easily. He learned Latin and Greek largely out of borrowed books, at one time wanting to be a minister. His motivation for this was not a desire for social advancement.[69] The son of the philosophizing cobbler was

---

[69] Taylor, a nephew of George Boole, criticizes Bell's treatment of this matter [A 7].

a deeply religious man, and there is no reason to suspect that his first choice of a career was based on anything other than religious grounds.

At first George Boole earned his living as an elementary school teacher, and at 20 he founded his own school. He occupied himself with mathematics only because books on mathematics were cheaper than those on the Classics.[70] He soon learned that the current textbooks were very poor, and therefore sought stimulation from the great men of his time. He studied Abel and Galois and, without any outside help, Laplace's *Mécanique Céleste*.

His "discovery of pure mathematics" is far more an insight of universal importance. He discovered that the symbolism of algebra is useful not merely for making statements about numbers and numerical variables. One can also introduce an algebra into the field of logic — an algebra related to the algebra of numbers. This discovery made the meaning of mathematical formalism clear: one can develop the laws of mathematical calculi without being restricted to special meanings — which is what Russell meant by "pure mathematics." Later the statements of the algebra can be interpreted in various branches of mathematics. Thus today "Boolean algebra" is important not only in the field of formal logic but also in the geometry of sets, the theory of probability, and the general theory of lattices.

Boole was stimulated to study the problems of logic by a dispute between the logician de Morgan, who was mathematically oriented, and the Scotch philosopher Sir William Hamilton[71] (1788-1856). In his little book *The Mathematical Analysis of Logic*, Boole developed the idea of *formal* logic. This notion had already occurred to Leibniz (p. 49), but it was Boole, the elementary school teacher, who first developed a practical algebra from the idea, nearly two hundred years later.

His book, which aroused the admiration of de Morgan, freed him from the drudgery of elementary teaching. He became professor of mathematics at Queens College in Cork. Six years later he published a more comprehensive work [VII 2], in which he gave a detailed development of his algebra of mathematical logic, and showed how it could be applied to the theory of probability, among other fields.

---

[70] This is no longer true. Are there, as a result, undiscovered mathematical geniuses who will never get a start?

[71] Not to be confused with the Irish mathematician Sir William Rowan Hamilton (1805-1865).

George Boole

This work of Boole's founded a new scientific discipline, formal logic, which may be considered either a part of philosophy or of mathematics, according to one's preference. For the mathematician, however, it is almost more important that with this work formalism in mathematics was given a new push. Peacock, in 1830 in his *Treatise on Algebra*, had already pointed out that the letters x, y, z, . . . in equations such as $x(y + z) = xy + xz$ and $x + y = y + x$ do not have to stand for numbers. For him they were abstract symbols which satisfied certain relations. Now this idea received a new impetus from the work of Boole. He made it clear that similar formalisms are also possible in logic.

Thus the way was opened for the liberation of mathematics from metaphysical notions. For the thinkers of earlier centuries, most of whom had been schooled in the Platonic teachings, the theorems of mathematics were statements about the world of ideas. When, later (in part through the discovery of the paradoxes of set theory[72]), mathematicians became suspicious of such unsupported metaphysical concepts, they tried to construct "formalistic" foundations for mathematics. Mathematics became the "science of formal systems," which consciously renounced any theory of the reality of its fundamental concepts. One may regret this turning away from the bright world of Plato, but it is based on the legitimate desire to eliminate all uncertain elements from mathematics. Thus, spurred on by Hilbert, modern proof theory was born. To it modern science owes many epistemologically important insights.[73]

We shall now discuss the fundamental ideas of Boole's *Investigation of the Laws of Thought* and the place of "Boolean algebra" in modern mathematics.

A new algebra

The concepts of our thought are expressed in different words in different languages. "State" is "Staat" in German, "civitas" in Latin. It is not the sequence of letters that matters, but the idea we associate with the sequence of letters. There is nothing to prevent us, Boole says ([VII 2], p. 26), from denoting an idea by a single letter. All that matters is that we do not change the meaning in the course of an argument. If we now replace combinations

---

[72] See Chapter IX and [A 12], Chapter X.
[73] See, for example, [A 12], Chapters X-XII.

of ideas by mathematical symbols like $+$, $-$, $\times$, etc., logical deductions can be "translated" into algebraic ones. This leads to Boole's first proposition.

Proposition I

All the operations of language, as an instrument of reasoning, may be conducted by a system of signs composed of the following elements, viz.:

First. Literal symbols, as x, y, etc., representing things as subjects of our conceptions.

Second. Signs of operation, as $+$, $-$, $\times$, standing for those operations of the mind by which the conceptions of things are combined or resolved so as to form new conceptions involving the same elements.

Third. The sign of identity, $=$.

These symbols of Logic are in their use subject to definite laws, partly agreeing with and partly differing from the laws of the corresponding symbols in the science of Algebra.

Let us begin with some simple examples. If the symbol x stands for "white things," the symbol y for "sheep," then the symbolic product xy stands for the class of things which belong both to x and to y: that is, white sheep. Clearly the commutative law

$$(1) \qquad xy = yx, xyz = xyz = yzx = \cdots$$

holds for this sort of product. This law (1) also holds in "ordinary" algebra. That is not, however, true of the proposition

$$(2) \qquad xx = x^2 = x \,.$$

Whatever class of things we think of x as representing, the "intersection" xx is always identical with x. The relation

$$(3) \qquad yx = xy = x$$

expresses a "containing." For example, (3) holds if x stands for the Germans, y for the Europeans: every European who is also a German, is a German.

The symbol $+$ is used to translate the conjunctions "and" and "or." If x stands for "men" and y for "women", then $x + y$ stands for "men and women," or the class of beings who are "men or women." Here "or" is to be understood in the sense of the Latin *vel*. "Either-or" (*aut-aut*) can also be expressed in the new symbolic language, as we shall show later. This language is superior to ordinary language in that it avoids such ambiguities as exist in the meaning of "or."

In the new algebra, the distributive law

$$(4) \qquad z(x + y) = zx + zy$$

also holds. Boole interprets this relation in the following way. Let z stand for "Europeans," x and y for "men" and "women." Then (4) says that "European men and women" are simply "European men" and "European women."

The minus sign is used to express an exception. If x stands for human beings and y for Asiatics, then $x - y$ is the class of human beings who are not Asiatics. Clearly the law

$$(4') \qquad z(x - y) = zx - zy$$

holds for the difference, in analogy with (4). If we use 1 to stand for the "universe," that is, for the set containing everything, and 0 for the "empty set," then we can get from (2) by formal rearrangement, the relation

$$(5) \qquad x - x^2 = 0 \, , \; x(1 - z) = 0 \, .$$

Here $1 - x$ is the class of things that do not belong to x, and thus $x(1 - x) = 0$ says there are no things which belong to x and do not belong to x.

Now we can also express the Latin *aut-aut* in our algebra. For "either x or y" means "x and not y or y and not x," that is

$$(6) \qquad x(1 - y) + y(1 - x) \, .$$

By a "logical function" we shall, with Boole ([VII 2], p. 71), understand, in what follows, an algebraic expression with one "variable" x, which is interpreted here as a "logical symbol." Similarly one can construct "logical functions" with several symbols, such as

$$f(x, y) = (x + y) \, (1 - x) \, .$$

Boole starts with the fact that every function $f(x)$ defined for numerical values of x can be represented in the form

$$(7) \qquad f(x) = f(1)x + f(0) \, (1 - x) \, .$$

This is easily seen if we substitute 0 or 1 for x in (7). Boole gives, as an example, the representation

(8)
$$\frac{1+x}{1+2x} = \frac{2}{3}x + 1 - x .$$

However, (8) is clearly valid only if no values of x but 0 and 1 are admitted.

From (7) it follows that for a corresponding function of two variables,

(9)
$$f(x, y) = f(1, y)x + f(0, y)(1 - x) .$$

If in (9) we replace $f(1, y)$ and $f(0, y)$, following (7), by
$$f(1, y) = f(1, 1)y + f(1, 0)(1 - y)$$
$$f(0, y) f(0, 1)y + f(0, 0)(1 - y)$$

we get

(10) $f(x, y) = f(1, 1)xy + f(1, 0)x(1 - y) + f(0, 1)(1 - x)y$
$$+ f(0, 0)(1 - x)(1 - y) .$$

An analogous result holds for a function of three variables under corresponding hypotheses:

(11) $f(x, y, z) = f(1, 1, 1)xzy$
$$+ f(1, 1, 0)xy (1 - z) + f(1, 0, 1)x(1 - y)z$$
$$+ f(1, 0, 0)x (1 - y) (1 - z) = f(0, 1, 1) (1 - x)yz$$
$$+ f(0, 1, 0) (1 - x)y(1 - z)$$
$$+ f(0, 0, 1) (1 - x) (1 - y)z$$
$$+ f(0, 0, 0) (1 - x) (1 - y) (1 - z) .$$

Boole uses this form of representation for functions in which x, y, and z are logical symbols. As before, 1 is to be understood as the "universe," 0 as the "empty set."

Now there is a serious objection to this procedure. Boole derived relation (7) under the assumption that x takes on only the values 0 and 1. If we interpret x, y and z as logical symbols, then this hypothesis must be "translated" as follows: for the logical symbols x, y, z, . . . , only the "universal set" 1 and the "empty set" 0 are to be submitted. Actually, however, Boole uses the representations (10) and (11) for *arbitrary* symbols x, y, z, ...

This procedure can be defended by pointing out that later "truth values" are introduced for the "secondary propositions" (see p. 79). Then the functions can be interpreted as statements about truth values. Thus Boole's procedure is justified. However, we can do without the "secondary propositions" at this point. We need merely recognize that in Boolean algebra only functions of a very simple type appear, for which (7), (10) and (11) are identities for all

$x, y, z, \ldots$. We do not need to represent any fractions like the one in (8) —
just (for one variable), functions of the form

(12) $$f(x) = \alpha x + \beta \, .$$

Because of (2) we can restrict ourselves to functions in which x occurs linearly.
Functions of the form (12), however, can always be written identically in
the form

(12′) $$f(x) = ax + b(1 - x) \, .$$

From this is follows at once that $a = f(1), b = f(0)$. Thus Boole is justified
in using relations (7), (9) and (11) for arbitrary logical symbols. One can
transform (12) into (12′) using algebraic laws which are valid for symbols
standing for statements too.

Boole shows by a simple example ([VII 2], p. 84) how (12) can be used in
a logical analysis. In the Mosaic Law those animals are called "clean" which
have two characteristics: they are ruminants and they have cloven hoofs
(Leviticus 11:1-3). Thus if we write x for clean animals, y for animals with
cloven hoofs, and z for ruminants, we have $x = yz$ or

(13) $$x - yz = 0 \, .$$

If we use (11) to express this function $f(x, y, z) = x - yz$ of three variables,
we get

(14)
$$0 \, xyz + xy(1 - z) + xz(1 - y) + x(1 - y)(1 - z)$$
$$- (1 - x)yz + 0(1 - x)y(1 - z) + 0(1 - x)(1 - y)z$$
$$+ 0(1 - x)(1 - y)(1 - z) = 0 \, .$$

This equation clearly holds only if all the terms which do not have the factor
0 vanish individually. Thus we have

(15)
$$xy(1 - z) = 0 \, , \quad xz(1 - y) = 0$$

$$x(1 - y)(1 - z) = 0 \, , \quad (1 - x)yz = 0 \, .$$

Relations (15) express the nonexistence of the following classes of things:
1. Animals which are clean and have cloven hoofs, but are not ruminants;
2. Animals which are clean and are ruminants, but do not have cloven hoofs;
3. Animals which are clean, but are not ruminants and do not have cloven
   hoofs;

4. Animals which are clean but have cloven hoofs and are ruminants.

Of course, it can be claimed that such insights can be deduced from the definition of clean animals without Boole's algebra. Nevertheless, the Bible does not consider such an analysis of the definition given in Leviticus 11:3 as trivial. In the following verses (4-7) it gives examples, to take the place of an analysis.

Until now we have substituted for the symbols x, y, z, . . . classes of *concrete* objects. Boole calls the logical formulas interpreted in this way, "concrete" or "primary" statements. In addition there are relations which combine *statements*. Such combinations Boole calls "abstract" or "secondary" statements.[74] We shall not go into any more detail concerning the theory of these secondary statements,[75] but shall limit ourselves to showing how Boole's algebra can be used in probability theory.

Application to probability

Classical probability theory is based on the notion of "equal likelihood."[76] If, of n "equally likely" events, m are "favorable" to the appearance of some characteristic, then the probability $p(x)$ of the appearance of this characteristic is

$$p = p(x) = m/n .$$

Here x stands for the "appearance of the characteristic." Correspondingly, the probability that the characteristic will not appear is

(16) $$p(1 - x) = n - m/n = 1 - m/n = 1 - p .$$

In (16) we have used Boole's terminology and denoted the event "complementary" to x by $(1 - x)$.

Furthermore, if x and y are events with probabilities p and q, then — if x and y are independent — pq is the probability that both events will happen. Accordingly we can associate with the compound events determined by x and y the corresponding probabilities by means of the following table:

---

[74] "The sun is shining" and "The earth is being warmed" are examples of "primary" statements; "If the sun is shining, the earth is being warmed," on the other hand, is secondary ([VII 2], p. 53).

[75] Modern propositional logic uses a terminology very different from Boole's.

[76] See, for example, *Wahrscheinlichkeitsrechnung*, by Wellnitz, Braunschweig 1954.

Event	Probability
xy	pq
$x(1 - y)$	$p(1-1q)$
$(1 - x)y$	$(1 - p)q$
$(1 - x)(1 - y)$	$(1 - p)(1 - q)$

(17)

The simple correspondences shown in this table can then be used to solve more complicated problems in the theory of probability. We cite only one example, given by Boole ([VII 2], p. 260). In doing so we use a modern notation for a "conditional probability."

The conditional probability that an event x will occur, under the hypothesis that y already occurred, is denoted by $p(x/y)$. For this probability we have

$$(18) \qquad p(x/y) = \frac{p(xy)}{p(y)} .$$

Now let p, q and r be the probabilities that the events x, y and z will occur. We ask for the probability that if either x or y occurs, y or z will occur.

Let u be the event that either x or y occurs, v the event that either y or z occurs. Then by (6)

$$(19) \qquad u = x(1 - y) + y(1 - x) \; ; v = y(1 - z) + z(1 - y) .$$

The probability $p(u/v)$ we are looking for can now be found from (18). For this, however, we need the probability $p(uv)$. Boolean algebra turns out to be a useful tool for computing it. From (19) we get

$$\begin{aligned} uv &= xy(1 - y)(1 - z) + yy(1 - x)(1 - z) \\ &+ xz(1 - y)(1 - y) + yz(1 - x)(1 - y) \\ &= xz(1 - y) + y(1 - x)(1 - z) . \end{aligned}$$

From (18), (20) and Table 17 we get for $p(u/v)$:

$$p(u/v) = \frac{p(uv)}{p(v)} = \frac{pr(1 - q) + q(1 - p)(1 - r)}{p(1 - q) + q(1 - p)} .$$

Boolean algebra today

Today we find the name of Boole not only in books on mathematical logic. We read of "Boolean Algebra" in books on algebra, lattice theory, the theory of probability, and information theory, and in publications on set theory. Only now, in the twentieth century, is the full fruitfulness of Boole's formalism apparent. It will underline the meaning of Boole's investigations, if we report briefly on the place of Boolean algebra in modern mathematics.

To make the generality of the concepts clear it is useful to replace the symbols used by Boole for plus and times by others which do not immediately make us think of operations on numbers. In the modern theory of lattices the synbols $\cup$ and $\cap$ are used in their place.[77] With the help of these symbols, abstract Boolean algebra can be defined as follows:

A set B with binary operations $\cap$ and $\cup$ is called a Boolean algebra if for the elements $a, b, c, \ldots$ of the set the following axioms hold:

1. $a \cap b = b \cap a$ $a \cup b = b \cup a$
2. $(a \cap b) \cap c = a \cap (b \cap c)$ $(a \cup b) \cup c = a \cup (b \cup c)$
3. $a \cap (a \cup b) = a$ $a \cup (a \cap b) = a$
4. $a \cap (b \cup c) = (a \cap b) \cup (a \cap c)$ $a \cup (b \cap c) = (a \cup b) \cap (a \cap c)$
5. B contains a zero element and a universal element with the properties $a \cup [0] = a$, $a \cap [1] = a$.
6. For each element x of B there is at least one element y of B[78] such that $x \cap y = [0]$, $x \cup y = [1]$.

One can easily convince himself that these six axioms are satisfied for Boole's symbols $x, y, z, \ldots$ if $x \cup y$ is replaced by $x + y$, $x \cap y$ by xy. In this way our axioms give us a foundation for the propositional calculus. They can also, however, be realized in quite a different way.

The simplest way of doing so is provided by the set consisting of the symbols 0 and 1, with the operations $\cup$ and $\cap$ defined by the following schema:[79]

(21)

$\cup$	0	1
0	0	1
1	1	1

$\cap$	0	1
0	0	0
1	0	1

---

[77] These are read "a intersection b" and "a union b", or, still more briefly, "a cap b" and "a cup b." See, for example, [VII 3].

[78] Elements x and y are called complementary.

[79] For the use of this schema in propositional logic see, for example, [A 12], p. 67.

George Boole

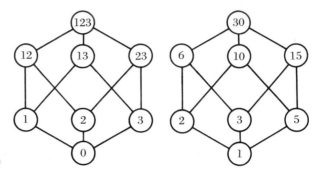

Fig. 17a and 17b

A further example is provided by the set consisting of the following eight digits or sequences of digits:

$$0; 1; 1; 2; 12; 13; 23; 123 .$$

Here the operations $\cup$ and $\cap$ are defined as follows: $a \cup b$ is the union, $a \cap b$ the intersection of the digits in a and b. The zero is the digit 0, the unity the sequence 123: [1] = 123. The laws of this simple Boolean algebra can be read off directly from Figure 17a. The segments drawn in the figure are to help in finding the union $a \cup b$ and the intersection $a \cap b$ of the elements a and b .

If we replace the digits 1, 2 and 3 by the primes 2, 3 and 5, and the sequences 12, 13, etc. of digits by the corresponding products $2 \cdot 3 = 6$, $2 \cdot 5 = 10$, etc., we get the schema for our algebra which is shown in Figure 17b. Now $a \cup b$ and $a \cap b$ have simple number theoretic meanings: $a \cup b$ is the least common multiple, $a \cap b$ the greatest common divisor of a and b. Here the number 1 turns out to be the "zero element."

Another Boolean algebra is the set of subsets of the points of a plane. Here $a \cap b$ is the intersection, $a \cup b$ the union of a and b. Axiom 4 (on page 81) can then be illustrated by Figures 18a and 18b.

We can now add to our definition of a Boolean algebra by explaining what is meant by a normed Boolean algebra: A Boolean algebra is said to be normed if to each element a in B can be assigned a number a' or $p(a)$ satisfying the conditions[80]

1. $0 \leq p(a) \leq 1$; $p([0]) = 0$, $p([1]) = 1$.
2. If $a \cap b = a$, then $p(a) \leqq p(b)$.
3. If $a \cap b = [0]$, then $p(a \cup b) = p(a) + p(b)$.

One example of such a normed Boolean algebra is the set of all measurable subsets of the unit square. The square itself is the unity, the empty set the zero. As norm we choose the area of a subset.

---

[80] For $a \cap b = a$ one can also write $a \subset b$: "a is contained in b."

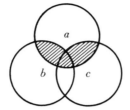 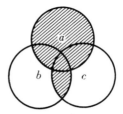

Fig. 18a and 18b

Another example is provided by the "events" of the theory of probability: here the probability $p(E)$ is the norm. Finally, one can interpret propositional logic as a normed Boolean algebra: here only the "truth values" 0 and 1 are admitted as norms.

These few references to the concepts of modern mathematics make it clear how fruitful was Boole's idea of interpreting the symbols of mathematics formally.

Weierstrass and his school

The teacher should let science develop before the eyes of his pupils. As it develops and takes form in the mind of the mature thinker, out of his fundamental ideas, so shall he present it, merely adjusting it to the youthful power of understanding.

K. Weierstrass[81]

[81] "On the Socratic method of teaching and its use in school teaching," in [VIII 1], vol. 3, pp. 315-329.

The arithmetization of analysis

One morning at the *Gymnasium* in Braunsberg in East Prussia — it was in the fifties of the last century — there was an absolutely inexcusable uproar. The teacher, Karl Weierstrass (1815-1899), had not appeared, and his class was kicking up an awful row. The principal hurried to the home of his young colleague and found him with curtains drawn and working by lamplight on a paper about Jacobi functions. He had worked all night and had not noticed that it was long past time to go to school.

In the long run it doesn't work — teaching school all day and searching at night for new paths in the theory of functions. Thus it was a good thing that Weierstrass let his great paper on the theory of Abelian functions appear in Crelle's Journal and not in the annual report of his high school, like his earlier papers. The paper he published in Crelle in 1854 was a success. The professor of mathematics at Königsberg procured an honorary doctorate for the Braunsberg school teacher, and travelled to the provincial town to present the diploma himself. Then the Prussian Minister of Culture gave Weierstrass a year's leave from his school duties, to give him time for his scientific work. Those who know Prussian thriftiness can judge from this the quality of the work of our teacher. Soon after this he became a professor at the Polytechnic School (now the Technical University) in Berlin-Charlottenburg, a little later professor at the Friedrich-Wilhelm University in Berlin.

In modern textbooks on function theory there are many theorems and methods of proof which we owe to Weierstrass. Of no less importance for twentieth-century mathematics, however, is the "arithmetization of analysis" he and his school introduced. In the notebooks of students of Karl Weierstrass we no longer find those dubious "infinitely small quantities" which were common in the textbooks of the 19th century. Weierstrass and his students "arithmetized" analysis: they reduced statements about limits to equations or inequalities between rational numbers.[82]

Weierstrass did not disown his past as a schoolmaster. At the university, too, he was a good teacher, and his ability as a mathematician and teacher attracted many students to Berlin. Among the most important of his students were Hermann Amandus Schwarz (1843-1921), Sonya Kovalevski (1850-1891),

---

[82] We cannot go into the objections Kronecker, and later the intuitionists, raised against Weierstrass' methods. There is more about this in [A 12], Chapter VII.

Georg Cantor (1845-1918), Magnus Gösta Mittag-Leffler (1846-1927), and David Hilbert (1862-1943).

As an illustration of the work of the school of Weierstrass, we present a previously unpublished letter of Hermann Amandus Schwarz. H. A. Schwarz became known for his many papers in the field of analysis and differential geometry. Later he was Weierstrass' successor in Berlin.

Our letter was written in 1870. At that time Schwarz was *Privatdozent* at Zurich. The letter contains a proof of the theorem, now familiar to every student, that a differentiable function whose derivative vanishes is constant. Nowadays we prove it using the mean-value theorem. When the *Privatdozent* H. A. Schwarz tells his friend Georg Cantor in Halle that he has found, in a few hours, the first *correct* proof of this theorem, we may safely believe him: he had probably studied the literature of his time thoroughly.

The first part of the letter presents results from notes of a lecture by Weierstrass. Then follows Scharz's own contribution. Thus the letter illustrates the working methods of Weierstrass and of his student and successor, H. A. Schwarz.

H. A. Schwarz to Georg Cantor

Hottingen near Zurich
February 25, 1870

My dear Georg,

The fact that I wrote to you at length yesterday is no reason why I should not write again today. For I have something to tell you which I am sure will interest you. A few hours ago I discovered what I think is the first rigorous proof of the following theorem:

If for every x such that $a \leq x \leq b$, $\lim\limits_{h \to 0} \dfrac{F(x+h) - F(x)}{h} = 0$, then

$F(x)$ is constant.

The separate steps I take from a lecture by Professor Weierstrass which I heard him give in 1861 at the Gewerbeinstitut.*

Let x be a continuous variable with bounds a and b, $f(x)$ a continuous, finite, single-valued function of x with a derivative $f'(x)$ which is also continuous, finite, and single-valued.

---

* Translator's Note: A technical institute, now called the Technical University, in Berlin.

I. *Lemma.* If, for a specific value x_o in the interior of the x-interval, the derivative of the function $f(x)$ is not zero, then there are always values of x in the neighborhood of x_o for which $f(x)$ is greater than $f(x_o)$, and also values for which $f(x)$ is smaller than $f(x_o)$.

Proof: let $f'(x_o)$ be unequal to zero and let x lie in the neighborhood of x_o; i. e., $x = x_o + h$. Then $f(x_o + h) - f(x_o)$ is made up of the two parts $f'(x_o)h + hh_1$, where h_1 is an otherwise entirely unknown function of h and x, of which we know only that for every value of x it becomes infinitely small as h does.

$$f(x_o + h) - f(x_o) = h(f'(x_o) + h_1).$$

$f'(x_o)$ is not zero. Let h_1 be made smaller than $f'(x_o)$ by making h small. This gives $|h| < \delta$. Then for every h for which $|h| < \delta$, $f'(x_o) + h_1$ has the same sign as $f'(x_o)$. Hence $f(x_o + h) - f'(x_o)$ changes sign when h does, q.e.d.

II. *Lemma.* If, for two specific values x_1 and x_2, $f(x_1) = f(x_2)$, then, between x_1 and x_2 there is at least one value x for which the first derivative is zero.

Proof: There is a value x_3 between x_1 and x_2 for which $f(x_3)$ is not equal to $f(x_1)$, since otherwise $f(x)$ would be constant. If $f(x_3)$ is smaller (larger) than $f(x_1)$, then there is a lower (an upper) bound for the values of $f(x)$ with $x_1 \leq x \leq x_2$. This bound is also a bound for an arbitrarily small region containing the point x_o. Because of continuity, the bound is actually attained at x_o. Thus $f'(x_o) = 0$, since otherwise, by Lemma I there would be both larger and smaller values of the function in the neighborhood of x_o, which contradicts the previously proved result that $f(x_o)$ is a minimum (maximum).

III. *Theorem.* If, throughout the interval $a \leq x \leq b$, $f'(x)$ is always positive and never zero, then $f(b) > f(a)$; $f(b)$ is the largest, $f(a)$ the smallest value that $f(x)$ can take on in this interval.

Proof: First, $f(b)$ is not equal to $f(a)$, since if it were, Lemma I would apply, and the conclusion of that lemma contradicts the hypothesis that $f'(x)$ is everywhere positive and nowhere zero. Nor is $f(x) = f(a)$ or $f(x) = f(b)$ anywhere in the interval. There exist an upper and a lower bound for the values of $f(x)$. This upper and lower bound are attained. (Argument as in II.) In the interior of $a \cdots b$, $f(x)$ has neither a maximum nor a minimum, since if it had, $f'(x_o)$ would have to be zero. Thus of the two values $f(a)$ and $f(b)$, one is the largest, the other the smallest. We need only decide which is larger.

Up to this point I have followed my notes on Weierstrass' lecture.

Now let $F(x)$ be a function about which we know nothing else but that it is finite, continuous, and single-valued, and that for every value of x ,

$$\lim_{h \to o} \frac{F(x + h) - F(x)}{h} = 0 .$$

From this follows the existence of the derivative, $F'(x)$, which is constant and has the value zero.

Now let k be a small positive quantity. Consider the functions

$$F(x) - F(a) - k(x - a)$$

and

$$F(x) - F(a) + k(x - a) .$$

The derivatives of these functions are $- k$ and k , respectively. For $x = a$, both functions are zero. By Theorem III and the corresponding theorem with $f'(x) < 0$, $F(b) - F(a) - k(b - a)$ is negative while $F(b) - F(a) + k(b - a)$ is positive. Thus in any case the difference $F(b) - F(a)$ lies between $k(b - a)$ and $- k(b - a)$. But[83] can make the quantity k arbitrarily small. Thus the difference $F(b) - F(a)$, whose value is entirely independent of the value of k , must equal zero. But b can be replaced by any value of x between a and b and the same conclusion drawn. Hence $F(x) = F(a)$, that is $F(x)$ is constant.

The proof above seems to me completely rigorous. It is the foundation of differential and integral calculus.

Be so good as to give the enclosed letter, whose contents may interest you too, to Mr. Hentschel.

Your true friend,
H. A. Schwarz

---

[83] We must supply "one."

Georg Cantor

In re mathematica ars proponendi questionem pluris facienda est quam solvendi.

G. Cantor[84]

[84] The third thesis in Cantor's doctoral dissertation.

A disputed "paradise"

It is not always a reflection on the author when the editors of a scientific journal hesitate to publish a paper submitted to them. It is precisely when the contents of the paper are out of the ordinary that a responsible editor will ask himself two or three times whether there is not an error somewhere. Thus, when a paper was submitted to Crelle's Journal on July 12, 1877, publication was postponed time and time again in favor of manuscripts submitted later, to the great annoyance of its author, Associate Professor Georg Cantor (1845-1918) of Halle.[85]

But Georg Cantor had himself been taken aback by the results of his research. On June 20, 1877, he had written to his friend, Richard Dedekind: *"Je le vois, mais je ne le crois pas."* Thus it is understandable that the gentlemen of Crelle's Journal at first did not want to believe what appeared in Cantor's "Contributions to the theory of sets."

This theory of sets is the creation of Georg Cantor. Stimulated by Weierstrass, his teacher, and Heine, he first published several papers on analysis. Then, however, he broke new ground. He compared infinite sets by establishing one-to-one correspondences between their elements. It turned out that such correspondences exist between sets of very different kinds. One can establish a one-to-one correspondence between an infinite set and a proper subset. For the set N of natural numbers 1, 2, 3, ... and the set E of even numbers this can be done as follows:

$$
\begin{array}{cccccc}
1 & 2 & 3 & 4 & 5 & 6 \quad \ldots \\
\updownarrow & \updownarrow & \updownarrow & \updownarrow & \updownarrow & \updownarrow \\
2 & 4 & 6 & 8 & 10 & 12 \quad \ldots
\end{array}
$$

Such a correspondence also exists, as one can easily show[86], between the set of natural numbers and the set R of all rational numbers. Cantor called two sets between whose elements there exists a one-to-one correspondence, equivalent, or of the same power. In 1875 he succeeded in proving that the set of points on a line was of higher power[87] than the sets N, E and R mentioned

---

[85] The paper did finally appear in Crelle's Journal in 1878.

[86] See, for example, [A 12], Chapter IV.

[87] M_1 is said to be of lower power than M_2 if there is a one-to-one correspondence between M_1 and a subset of M_2, but not between M_1 and M_2 itself.

above. This paper Crelle's Journal accepted without objection, but the editors hesitated when he submitted a proof in 1877 that sets of points of different dimensions may also be equivalent: for example, the sets of points in a segment and in a square.

David Hilbert once called Cantor's theory of sets a "paradise from which no one must be permitted to drive us."[88] This statement of the great mathematician does more than show his frank enthusiasm for Cantor's beautiful theory. It also makes it clear that our stay in that paradise is threatened in one way or another. The fact that his influential Berlin colleague Kronecker declined to accept his work lay like a dark shadow over the life of the gifted and sensitive Halle mathematician. It was Kronecker, undoubtedly, who was responsible for the delay in the publication of the fundamental paper of 1877. He objected to Cantor's use of the "actually infinite." He and his followers, the intuitionists, held that one can not consider an infinite set as given in its entirety.

What we call infinite is, according to Poincaré, "merely the possibility of continually constructing new objects, no matter how many have already been constructed."[89] Consistent adherence to this fundamental principle leads to the view that a secure mathematics can deal only with countable sets. These objections to Cantor's theory assumed added importance when the paradoxes of set theory were discovered at the turn of the century. Cantor had intentionally made the concept of a set very broad and had admitted as elements of sets all "objects of perception or thought." It now appeared that such notions as the set of all sets led to contradictions.[90] Russell, the discoverer of these paradoxes, was at once able to come to the aid of the young mathematical theory: if the notion of a set is restricted and aggregates which are too vague are excluded, then Russell's paradoxes are avoided.

Later the formalists of the school of Hilbert showed that an axiomatic foundation of set theory is quite possible. To be sure, this does not dispose of the objections of the radical intuitionists. However, it would be fair to say that Cantor's theory of sets is as secure (or as insecure) as classical analysis.

Thus, Cantor won, from the mathematicians of the twentieth century, the recognition that not all his contemporaries would grant him.

---

[88] [A 8], p. 371.
[89] Acta Math. 32, 1909, p. 156.
[90] See [A 12], Chapter VI.

To be sure, the discussion of the paradoxes of set theory led research in the foundation of mathematics a long way from the classical view of the nature of mathematics so passionately defended by Cantor. Intuitionists and formalists are united in their effort to eliminate all metaphysical elements from the foundations of the exact sciences. For example, in order to achieve a secure and generally accepted development of mathematics, ontological statements about mathematical objects are eliminated. Modern axioms are not statements about any sort of reality, but rather the foundations of formal mathematical systems. They must be consistent and independent. This restriction springs not from a malicious nihilistic whim but from the desire for absolute certainty.

Georg Cantor, schooled in Plato and the scholastics, thought differently about the matter. For him, mathematics was a sort of auxiliary science to metaphysics, and his set theory was actually a part of metaphysics.

In this connection we quote several sentences from a previously unpublished letter (dated February 2, 1896) from Georg Cantor to Father Thomas Esser in Rome:[91]

> The establishing of the principles of mathematics and the natural sciences is the responsibility of metaphysics. Hence metaphysics must look on them as her children and as her servants and helpers, whom she must not let out of her sight, but must watch over and control, as the queen bee in a hive sends into the garden thousands of industrious bees, to suck nectar from the flowers and then together, under her supervision, to turn it into precious honey, and who must bring her, from the wide realm of the material and spiritual world, the building blocks to finish her palace. . . . The general theory of sets, which you will find in the paper "On the lore of transfinite numbers," as well as in the first article of the work *Contributions to the Foundations of Transfinite Set Theory*, which I have begun, belongs entirely to metaphysics. You can easily convince yourself of this by testing the categories of cardinal number and ordinal type, these fundamental concepts of set theory, with respect to the degree of their generality, and also

---

[91] We quote from the first draft of the letter. In Cantor's notebook many things are crossed out, corrected, etc. This explains the somewhat uneven style. It is to be assumed that the clean copy read somewhat differently.

notice that the reasoning about them is quite pure, so that fancy has no room for play.

This is in no way changed by the pictures which I, like all metaphysicians, sometimes make use of to explain metaphysical concepts. Nor does the fact that my work appears in mathematical journals affect its metaphysical character and content.

It is part of the tragedy of our investigator's life,[92] so full of disappointments, that his own theory gave rise to a new concept of mathematics which, for good reasons, put an end to basing the exact sciences on metaphysics.

Among the friends and admirers of Georg Cantor was the Berlin high school teacher Goldscheider. On one occasion he asked the Halle professor several questions about the latter's theory of sets. Cantor answered with a completeness that is amazing to us today. Did he have so much more time than a modern professor, or may we take it as proof of his good nature, that one of his letters to Goldscheider turned into a small, handwritten textbook?

This letter of June 18, 1886, introduces Cantor's investigations.

Georg Cantor to F. Goldscheider

Halle, June 18, 1886

To Mr. F. Goldscheider in Berlin

I. Given a certain set M, consisting of concrete things or abstract concepts, which we call elements; if we disregard the nature of the elements and the order in which they are given, there remains a certain general notion, which I call the *power* of M or the *cardinal number* corresponding to M.

II. Two fixed sets M and M_1 are called equivalent, in symbols $M \sim M_1$, if it is possible to put them into one-to-one correspondence, element by element, according to some rule. If $M \sim M_1$ and $M_1 \sim M_2$, then $M \sim M_2$.

Examples:

1. The set of colors of the rainbow is $\sim$ the set of tones in an octave.

---

[92] [IX 1] contains a biography of Georg Cantor by A. Fraenkel.

2. The set of fingers on my two hands is $\sim$ the set

$$a$$
$$b \quad c$$
$$d \quad e \quad f$$
$$g \quad h \quad i \quad k \ .$$

3. The set (Y) of all real, positive whole numbers is $\sim$ the set $(n + mi)$ of all complex whole numbers, $\sim$ the set (n/m) of all real, rational numbers, $\sim$ the set of all real and complex *algebraic* numbers. (Crelle, vol. 77, p. 258.)

4. The set of all points on a line AB is $\sim$ the set of all points on another line, $\sim$ the set of all points of an arbitrary regular curve, but also $\sim$ the set of all points of a surface, a solid figure, etc. (Crelle, vol. 84, p. 242).

III. From I and II it follows that equivalent sets always have *the same power*, and conversely, that sets with *the same cardinal number* are equivalent.

IV. If two sets M and N are joined to form a set S, and two sets M_1 and N_1, equivalent to M and N respectively, are joined to form a set S_1, then $S \sim S_1$. If the power of M and M_1 is denoted by a, the power of N and N_1 by a', and the power of S and S_1 by b, then we express the relation between a, a' and b by the equation

$$a + a' = b \ .$$

This contains the definition of the sum of two powers or cardinal numbers.

It is easy to see that

$$a + a' = a' + a$$

$$a + (a' + a'') = (a + a') + a'' \ ,$$

i.e. the *commutative* and *associative* laws hold for the *addition* of x cardinal numbers.

V. If in a set N of power a' one replaces *each element* by *a set* of power a, one obtains a new set whose power we shall call c. Then c is called the product of the *multiplicand* a and the *multiplier* a', in symbols

$$a \cdot a' = c.$$

It can be proved that

$$a \cdot a' = a' \cdot a$$
$$a \cdot (a' \cdot a'') = (a \cdot a') \cdot a''.$$

Thus the *commutative* and *associative* laws also hold for the *multiplication* of powers.

VI. These basic laws apply as well to *finite* as to *actually infinite* sets and their powers or cardinal numbers. For *finite* cardinals it is easily seen that in an equation

$$a + a' = b$$

b is never *equal* to either of the summands a and a'. For *actually infinite* cardinals, however, it is easily proved that the last theorem does not hold. For example, if a is any *actually infinite* cardinal,

$$1 + a = a$$
$$a + a = a \cdot 2 = a$$
$$a \cdot a = a$$

and so forth. There is no contradiction to be found in this if one goes back to the definitions in I and II. In general, why should a set M not have the same property, called here its power, as an extended set $M + N$?

It is our *familiarity* with *finite* sets that makes us at first find difficulties here. Yet the situation is *analogous* to that of the general concept "man," which applies to my person at this moment just as much as it did 40 years ago, though I have grown somewhat and changed a lot since then.

VII. Now I shall acquaint you with the general notion of a *well-ordered* set, as it is defined on page 4 of the "Foundations" (i.e. the fifth of the papers in Math. Ann., "On infinite linear point sets," vol XXI, p. 548).

Examples:

1. $(a, b, c, d, e, f, g, h, i, k)$ is a well-ordered set, in contrast to

$$a$$
$$b \quad c$$
$$d \quad e \quad f$$
$$g \quad h \quad i \quad k \; .$$

Both sets consist of the same elements, and hence have the same power.

2. The sequence of finite cardinals in their natural order:

$$(1, 2, 3, \ldots, n, \ldots)$$

3. The set of all positive rational numbers arranged in the following order:

$$(\tfrac{1}{1}, \tfrac{1}{2}, \tfrac{2}{1}, \tfrac{1}{3}, \tfrac{3}{1}, \tfrac{1}{4}, \tfrac{2}{3}, \tfrac{3}{2}, \tfrac{4}{1}, \tfrac{1}{5}, \tfrac{5}{1}, \tfrac{1}{6}, \tfrac{2}{5}, \tfrac{3}{4}, \tfrac{4}{3}, \tfrac{5}{2}, \tfrac{6}{1}, \ldots)$$

The rule for ordering here is that of two positive rational numbers m/n and m'/n' in *reduced* form,[93] the first has a *lower* or *higher* rank than the second according as $m + n$ is smaller or larger than $m' + n'$; however, if $m + n = m' + n'$, the ranks depend on the relative sizes of m and m'.[94] In *this* ordering, every non-empty subset has a first element. With the usual order relation $(a < b)$ this is not the case: the set of all rational numbers of the form $1/n$ has no smallest element.

4. $(1, 3, 5, 7, 9, \ldots, 2, 4, 6, 8, 10, \ldots)$
Here the finite cardinals are thought of with the odd numbers in their natural order, followed by the even numbers in their natural order.

5. $(3, 5, 7, 9, 11, \ldots, 2, 4, 6, 8, 10, \ldots, 1)$.
This is also the set of all finite whole numbers as a *well-ordered* set, but here 1 has the highest rank.

6. Consider a system of elements a_{mn} with two finite but unbounded indices, and determine the rank by the following rule: of two

---

[93] That is, in lowest terms.

[94] One can also say briefly: $a \prec b$ (a precedes b) when, in Cantor's sense, a has a lower rank than b.

elements a_{mn} and $a_{m'n'}$, the first has lower or higher rank than the second according as m is smaller or larger than m'; if, however, $m = m'$, the order of ranks is determined by the sizes of n and n'. This gives the following well-ordered set:

$$(a_{11}, a_{12}, \ldots, a_{1n}, \ldots, a_{21}, a_{22}, \ldots, a_{2n}, \ldots$$
$$\ldots, a_{31}, a_{32}, \ldots, a_{3n}, \ldots$$
$$\ldots, a_{m1}, a_{m2}, \ldots, a_{mn}, \ldots$$
$$\ldots, a_{m+1,1}, a_{m+1,2}, \ldots, a_{m+1,n}, \ldots \ldots)$$

VIII. If, in a *well-ordered* set M, we disregard the nature of the elements but *not* the order in which they are given, we get a certain general notion which in the "Foundations" I call the number of elements in the well-ordered set M, but which I here prefer to call the *ordinal number* of the well-ordered set M, or the *form* or *type* of the well-ordered set M.

IX. I call two well-ordered sets M and M_1 *similar* or *conformal**** — in symbols, $M \, cf \, M_1$ — if there is a one-to-one correspondence between the two such that the relation between the ranks of any *two* elements of M is the same as the relation between the ranks of the *corresponding* elements of M_1. There is *at most one* such correspondence, whereas if there is one correspondence of the kind used in the definition of equivalence in II, there are *many*.

Two *similar* well-ordered sets are necessarily equivalent, hence of the same power.

If $M \, cf \, M_1$ and $M_1 \, cf \, M_2$, then $M \, cf \, M_2$.

Examples:
1. The well-ordered sets $(a, b, c, d, e, f, g, h, i, k)$ and $(a', b', c', d', e', f', g', h', i', k')$ are similar. In the one-to-one correspondence, a corresponds to a', b to b', $\ldots$, k to k'.
2. The well-ordered sets introduced in VII 2 and VII 3 are similar.

---

* Translator's note: this word, a literal translation of the German *konform*, is not used in this sense in English.

3. The two well-ordered sets

$$(1, 3, 5, 7, \ldots, 2, 4, 6, 8, \ldots)$$

and

$$(a_2, a_4, a_6, a_8, \ldots, a_1, a_3, a_5, a_7, \ldots)$$

are similar. In the correspondence, 1 must correspond to a_2, 3 to a_4, 5 to a_6, etc., 2 to a_1, 4 to a_3, 6 to a_5, etc. No other one-to-one correspondence between the sets (such as the one, for example, in which n in the first set corresponds to a_n in the second) satisfies the requirement that the relation between the ranks of *any two* elements of the first set is the same as that between the ranks of the corresponding elements of the second.

4. The two well-ordered sets

$$(1, 2, 3, \ldots, n, \ldots)$$

and

$$(2, 3, 4, \ldots, n+1, \ldots)$$

of which the first is a *part* of the second, are similar. On the other hand, neither is similar to the well-ordered set

$$(2, 3, 4, \ldots, 1),$$

although this last set consists of exactly the same numbers as the first of the three.

The last of these three well-ordered sets has a *highest*, "last" element in the sense of rank, namely, 1; the first two have no "last" element.

X. From VIII and IX it follows that *similar* well-ordered sets have *the same* ordinal number, form, or type, and conversely, that well-ordered sets with the same ordinal number are similar. Thus the well-ordered sets

$$(1, 2, 3, \ldots, n, \ldots)$$

and

$$(2, 3, 4, \ldots, n+1, \ldots)$$

have *the same* ordinal number, although the second is only a part of the first. On the other hand, the well-ordered sets

$$(1, 2, 3, \ldots, n, \ldots)$$

and

$$(2, 3, 4, \ldots, n + 1, \ldots, 1)$$

have different ordinal numbers or types, *although* they are made up of *the same* elements.

XI. The ordinal type or number of the well-ordered set

$$(1, 2, 3, \ldots, n, \ldots)$$

I denote by ω.

XII. If two well-ordered sets M and N of ordinal types α and α' are combined to form a new well-ordered set γ in such a way that the elements of M and N preserve their rank relationships, but all the elements of M have lower ranks than any element of N, the ordinal number β of γ is called the sum of the ordinal numbers α and α' of M and N:

$$\alpha + \alpha' = \beta .$$

Here α is called the *augend*, α' the *addend*.
In general, $\alpha + \alpha'$ and $\alpha' + \alpha$ are different. If α and α' are both finite, $\alpha + \alpha' = \alpha' + \alpha$. On the other hand, it is always the case that

$$\alpha + (\alpha' + \alpha'') = (\alpha + \alpha') + \alpha'' .$$

Thus while the *commutative* law does not hold in general for addition of *ordinal numbers*, the *associative* law does.

Examples:

1. $1 + \omega = \omega$, while $\omega + 1$ is different from ω.

2. The well-ordered sets in VII 2 and VII 3 have the same ordinal number, ω.

3. The well-ordered set in VII 4 has the ordinal number $\omega + \omega$, and that in VII 5 the ordinal number $\omega + \omega + 1$.

XIII. If *every* element in a well-ordered set N of order type α' is replaced by a well-ordered set of order type α, the result is a new well-ordered set P whose order type γ is called the product, $\alpha \cdot \alpha'$, of the *multiplicand* α and the *multiplier* α' :

$$\alpha \cdot \alpha' = \gamma .$$

In the "Foundations" the *multiplier* was written first, then the multiplicand; but the opposite order is preferable.

Here, too, $\alpha \cdot \alpha'$ and $\alpha' \cdot \alpha$ are in general different. If α and α' are finite ordinal numbers, then $\alpha \cdot \alpha' = \alpha' \cdot \alpha$. On the other hand, it is always true that $\alpha \cdot (\alpha' \cdot \alpha'') = (\alpha \cdot \alpha') \cdot \alpha''$. For example, let $\alpha = \omega$, $\alpha' = 2$. Here N is $(a,b,)$, say. Replace a by $(a_1, a_2, \ldots, a_n, \ldots)$ of type ω, b by $(b_1, b_2, \ldots, b_n, \ldots)$ of type ω. The result is the well-ordered set P:

$$(a_1, a_2, \ldots, \ a_n, \ldots, \ b_1, b_2, \ldots, \ b_n \ldots)$$

whose order type is $\omega \cdot 2$.

On the other hand let $\alpha = 2$, $\alpha' = \omega$. Then N is, say, $(n_1, n_2, \ldots, n_k, \ldots)$. If n is replaced by the well-ordered set (p_k, q_k) of type 2, the resulting well-ordered set P is

$$(p_1, q_1, p_2, q_2, \ldots, \ p_n, q_n, \ldots)$$

which is of type $2 \cdot \omega$. However, since the last set has type ω, we conclude that

$$2 \cdot \omega = \omega .$$

Thus the numbers $\omega + \omega$ and $\omega + \omega + 1$ which occur in XII can also be written $\omega \cdot 2$ and $\omega \cdot 2 + 1$. The example of a well-ordered set given in VII 6 clearly has ordinal number $\omega \cdot \omega = \omega^2$.

XIV. The *power* of the set of all finite numbers is the *smallest* transfinite power, just as ω is the *smallest* transfinite ordinal number. I call this power the *first* transfinite power or, more simply, the *first* power, and denote it by $\overset{*}{\omega}$. In general, I denote the power of a well-ordered set of ordinal type α by $\overset{*}{\alpha}$. Clearly

$$(\omega \overset{*}{+} 1) = (\omega \overset{*}{+} 2) = \cdots = \overset{*}{\omega} .$$

also,

$$(\omega \overset{*}{\cdot} 2) = (\omega \cdot \overset{*}{2} + 1) = (\omega \cdot \overset{*}{2} + 2) = \cdots = \overset{*}{\omega}$$

and
$$\overset{*}{\omega}{}^2 = \overset{*}{\omega}.$$

Thus we see that when we construct the ordinal numbers

$$\omega, \ \omega + 1, \ldots, \ \omega \cdot 2, \ \omega \cdot 2 + 1, \ldots$$

the corresponding powers at first remain the same.

XV. The collection of *all* ordinal numbers which are the ordinal types of sets of power $\overset{*}{\omega}$ I call the *second number class*:

$$\omega, \omega + 1, \ldots, \omega^\mu \mu_0 + \omega^{\mu-1}\mu_1 + \cdots + \omega\mu_{\mu-1} + \mu_\mu, \ldots, \omega^\omega, \ldots, \omega^{\omega^\omega}, \ldots.$$

This second number class itself forms, in its natural order, a well-ordered set whose order type I call Ω ; Ω is the *smallest* number in the third number class. The power $\overset{*}{\Omega}$ of the second number class is not $= \overset{*}{\omega}$ again but, as I prove in section 13 of the "Foundations," the *next* power greater than $\overset{*}{\omega}$.

XVI. While the *finite* ordinal numbers obey *the same* laws as the finite cardinals (which is why the difference has not previously been made clear in number theory), the difference between *transfinite ordinal and transfinite cardinal* numbers becomes sharp and clear.

Example of an uncountable set

In Cantor's letter of June 18, 1886, to Goldscheider, the fundamental ideas of set theory up to well-ordering are developed. Strangely enough, however, the existence of sets with different powers is merely mentioned, not proved. For that reason we shall supplement the letter by proving that the set of points in any interval is *uncountable*, that is, does not have the same power as the set N of natural numbers. It is through this proof that the meaning of Cantor's concepts first becomes clear: *there are* sets of different powers, and hence the notion of power is adapted to making distinctions in the previously quite inaccessible realm of the infinite.

Usually the theorem referred to is proved by Cantor's diagonal process. Here we reproduce Cantor's less familiar first proof. His theorem[95] reads:

---

[95] Crelle's Journal, 77, 1874, pp. 258-262, or [IX 1], p. 115 ff.

Let

(1)
$$a_1, a_2, a_3, \ldots$$

be an infinite series[96] of distinct real numbers, constructed according to any rule. Then in any given interval (c,d)[97] there is a number y (and hence infinitely many such numbers) which does not occur in series (1).

To prove this we call the first two numbers in series (1) which lie in the interval (c,d) c_1 and d_1. Similarly, c_{n+1} and d_{n+1} are the first two numbers in series (1) which lie in the interval (c_n, d_n) $(n = 1, 2, 3, \ldots)$. We must now distinguish two possibilities:

1. There are only a finite number of intervals (c_n, d_n): $n = 1, 2, \ldots, N$. Then in the last interval there are not two numbers of (1) but at most one. In that case there is certainly a number y in this interval (hence also in (c, d)) which does not appear in (1).

2. There are infinitely many intervals (c_n, d_n). Then the bounded sequences c_n and d_n are respectively monotone increasing and decreasing. Hence there exist limits

$$C = \lim_{n \to \infty} c_n, \quad D = \lim_{n \to \infty} d_n.$$

If $C = D$, this number is contained in every interval (c_n, d_n) of the sequence. Thus it is not equal to any of the numbers in (1). If $C \neq D$, the same is true of every number in the (closed) interval $[C, D]$. Thus in both cases there is at least one number y which is not contained in (1).

---

[96] We say "sequence" today.
[97] (a, b) denotes an open interval, $[A, B]$ a closed interval.

Bibliography

The following list contains a few works on the history of mathematics which are of particular importance, but mainly works used in the writing of this book. More detailed accounts, including information on source materials, are contained in the books whose numbers are followed by asterisks.

A. General works on the history of mathematics

1. H. Hankel, *Zur Geschichte der Mathematik in Altertum und Mittel-alter*, Leipzig (1878)

2. M. Cantor, *Vorlesungen über Geschichte der Mathematik*, 4 vols. (1880)

3.*J. Tropfke, *Geschichte der Elementarmathematik*, 7 vols., Leipzig (1903), Berlin (1940)

4. G. Kovalevski, *Grosse Mathematiker*, Munich (1938)

5.*O. Becker and J. Hofmann, *Geschichte der Mathematik*, Bonn (1951)

6. F. von Krbek, *Eingefangenes Unendlich, Bekenntnis zur Geschichte der Mahtematik*, Leipzig (1952)

7. E. T. Bell, *Men of Mathematics*, 2 vols., Melbourne-London-Baltimore (1953)

8.*O. Becker, *Grundlagen der Mathematik*, Munich (1954)

9. J. E. Hofmann, *Geschichte der Mathematik*, 3 vols., Berlin (1953-1957). English translation of Vol. I as *History of Mathematics*, New York (1957) and of Vols. II, III as *Classical Mathematics*, New York and London (1959)

10. H. Steinhaus, *Mathematical Snapshots*, Second Printing, London-Paris (1951)

11. O. Becker, *Grösse und Grenze der Mathematischen Denkweise*, Munich (1960)

12. H. Meschkowski, *Wandlungen des Mathematischen Denkens — eine Einführung in die Grundlagenprobleme der Mathematik*, 2nd enlarged edition, Braunschweig (1960). An English translation is in press.

Bibliography

B. Bibliography for individual chapters

I   1. T. L. Heath, *A History of Greek Mathematics*, Oxford (1921)

I   2. J. L. Heiberg, *Geschichte der Mathematik und Naturwissenschaften im Altertum*, Munich (1925)

I   3. C. Thaer, *Die Elemente von Euklid*, Leipzig (1933)

I   4. K. Reidemeister, *Das exakte Denken bei den Griechen*, Hamburg (1949)

I   5. G. Hauser, *Geometrie der Griechen von Thales bis Euklid*, Lucerne (1955)

I   6. B. L. van der Waerden, *Science Awakening*, English translation by Arnold Dresden, with additions of the author, New York (1961)

I   7. O. Becker, *Das Mathematische Denken in der Antike*, Göttingen (1957)

I   8. H. Diels, *Die Fragmente der Vorsokratiker*, Hamburg (1957)

I   9. S. Heller, *Die Entdeckung der stetigen Teilung durch die Pythagoreer*, Abhandlungen der D. Ak. d. Wiss., Klasse f. Math., Phys., u. Technik (1958), No. 6

I 10. H. Meschkowski, *Differenzengleichungen*, Göttingen (1959)

II   1. T. L. Heath, *The Works of Archimedes*, Dover Publications, New York (no date)

II   2. E. I. Dijksterhuis, *Die Intergrationsmethoden von Archimedes*, Nordisk Mat. Tidskrift 2 (1954), pp. 5-26

II   3. W. F. Kagen, *Archimedes*, Leipzig (1955)

III   1. *Schriften des Nikolaus von Cues*, published in German translation by arrangement with the Heidelberger Ak. d. Wiss., ed. Ernst Hoffmann

Volume 11: *Die Mathematischen Schriften*, translated by Josepha Hofmann, introduction and notes by J. E. Hofmann, Hamburg (1950)

III 2. Nicholas of Cusa, *Die Kunst der Vermutung*, a selection from his works, Bremen (1957)

IV 1. Pascal, *Vermächtnis eines Grossen Herzens*, the smaller works, translated (into German) and edited by W. Rüttenauer, Leipzig (1938)

IV 2. Pascal, *Oeuvres Complètes*, texte établi et annoté par Jacques Chevalier, Librairie Gallimard (1954)

IV 3. P. Montel, *Pascal Mathémematicien*, Paris (1951)

V 1. G. W. Leibniz, *Mathematische Schriften*, 7 vols. ed. C. J. Gerhardt, Berlin (1849-1890)

V 2. G. W. Leibniz, *Der Briefwechsel mit Mathematikern*, ed. C. J. Gerhardt, Berlin (1899)

V 3. G. W. Leibniz, *Hauptschriften zur Grundlegung der Philosophie I*, Leipzig (no date)

V 4. D. Mahnke, *Neue Einblicke in die Entdeckungsgeschichte der Höheren Analysis*, Abh. Pr. Ak. d. Wiss. (1925), Phys. math. Klasse, No. 1, Berlin (1926)

V 5. J. E. Hofmann and H. Wieleitner, *Differenzenrechnung bei Leibniz*, mit Zusätzen von D. Mahnke, Sitzungsber. der Pr. Ak. d. Wiss., Math.-Phys. Klasse (1931), pp. 562-600

V 6. D. Mahnke, *Zur Keimesgeschichte der Leibnizschen Differentialrechnung*, Sitzungsber. der Ges. zur Beford. der ges. Naturwiss. zu Marburg, Berlin (1932), pp. 31-36

V 7. J. E. Hofmann, *Die Entwicklungsgeschichte der Leibnizschen Mathematik*, Munich (1949)

V 8. J. E. Hofmann, *Zur Entdeckungsgeschichte der Höheren Analysis im 17. Jahrhundert*, Math. Phys. Semesterberichte 1 (1950), pp. 220-255

V 9. J. O. Fleckenstein, *Der Prioritätsstreit Zwischen Leibniz und Newton*, Basel and Stuttgart (1956)

Bibliography

VI   1. C. F. Gauss, *Werke*, ed. Gesellschaft der Wiss., Göttingen (since 1876)

VI   2. E. Worbs, *Carl Friedrich Gauss — Ein Lebensbild*, Leipzig (1955)

VI   3. C. F. *Gauss, Gedenkband Anlässlich des 100. Todestages am 23. Februar 1955*, herausgegeben von H. Reichardt, Berlin (1955)

VI   4. F. W. Levi, *Gauss und das Raumproblem*, Math. Phys. Semesterberichte V (1957), pp. 191-199

VII   1. George Boole, *The Mathematical Analysis of Logic*, Cambridge (1847)

VII   2. George Boole, *An Investigation of the Laws of Thought* (1854), republished by Dover Publications, Inc. (1951)

VII   3. H. Hermes, *Einführung in die Verbandstheorie*, Berlin-Göttingen-Heidelberg (1955)

VII   4. A. M. Jaglom, J. M. Jaglom, *Wahrscheinlichkeit und Information*, Berlin (1960)

VII   5. Celebration of the centenary of *The Laws of Thought* by George Boole, Proc. Royal Irish Ac., vol. 57, Sec. A, No. 6 (1955)

VIII   1. K. Weierstrass, *Mathematische Werke*, Berlin (1894)

VIII   2. H. A. Schwarz, *Gesammelte Mathematische Abhandlungen*, Berlin (1890)

IX   Georg Cantor, *Gesammelte Abhandlungen*, ed. E. Zermelo, Berlin (1932)

Index of names

Abel, 62, 63, 73, 86
Archimedes, 11, **13-23**, 26, 28-31, 106
Archytas, 14

Becker, 105, 106
Bell, 72, 105
Bessel, 63
Boethius, 26
Bolyai, 48, 63
Boole, 49, **71-83**, 108

Cantor, G., 87, **91-104**, 105
Cantor, M., 108
Cauchy, 57

Dedekind, 92
Democritus, 15
Diels, 106
Dijkerhuis, 106

Eratosthenes, 15, 20
Esser, 94
Euclid, 11, 14, 34, 44, 106
Eudoxus, 14, 15

Fibonacci, 10
Fleckenstein, 107
Fraenkel, 95

Galloys, 57
Galois, 73
Gauss, **61-69**, 108
Goldscheider, 95, 103
Guericke, 48

Hamilton, W., 73
Hamilton, W. R., 73
Hankel, 105
Hauser, 106

Heath, 106
Heiberg, 15, 106
Heine, 92
Heller, 8, 10, 11, 106
Hentschel, 89
Hermes, 108
Herodotus, 2
Hieron, 14
Hilbert, 74, 87, 93
Hippasus, 6, 8
Hoffman, E., 106
Hofmann, J., 51, 105, 106
Hofmann, J. E., 28, 29, 105-107
Huygens, 48, 50

Iamblichus, 6

Jacobi, 63, 86
Jaglom, A. M., 108
Jaglom, J. M., 108

Kagan, 106
Kovalevski, G., 105
Kovalevski, S., 86
Kronecker, 86, 93

Laplace, 73,
Leibniz, 35, **47-59**, 73, 107
Levi, F. W., 108
Lobachevski, 48, 63

Mahnke, 107
Meschkowski, 105, 106
Mittag-Leffler, 87
Montel, 107
De Morgan, 73

Newton, 48, 49, 107
Nicholas of Cusa, **25-31**, 106, 107
Nichomachus of Gerasa, 3

Index of names

Pascal, B., 11, **33-45**, 48, 50-52, 107
Pascal-Périer, G., 34, 35,
Peacock, 74
Pfaff, 63
Philolaus, 1
Plato, 14, 26, 74, 94
Plutarch, 14
Poincaré, 93
Polycrates, 2
Pythagoras, **1-11**, 26, 106

Reidemeister, 106
Rolle, 57
Rümcker, 63
Russell, B., 71, 72, 93

Schopenhauer, 15
Schumacher, 63
Schwarz, H. A., 86-89, 108

Stegmüller, 27
Steinhaus, 105

Taylor, 72
Thaer, 106
Theon of Smyrna, 9
Tropfke, 105

Varignon, 57, 58

van der Waerden, 9, 11, 106
von Krbek, 105
von Waltershausen, 62

Weierstrass, 57, 63, **85-89**, 92, 108
Wellnitz, 79
Wieleitner, 51, 107
Worbs, 62, 108

This book is set in Monotype Modern No. 8,
with headings in Franklin Gothic.
The composition is by Holmes Typography.
The book was designed by Jean Swift,
printed by Halliday Lithograph Corporation
and bound at Colonial Press.
The paper is Warren's Silkote.